ANNA BILEY

Birds Hold our Secrets

a caritas story of grief
and remembering

LOTUS
LIBRARY

BIRDS HOLD OUR SECRETS...

First published in Great Britain in 2019 by Lotus Library
Copyright © Anna M. Biley, 2019
Internal illustrations © Sarah Hough
www.sarahhough.com
All rights reserved

A CIP catalogue record for this book is available from the British Library.

ISBN 978-1-7331232-0-4

Managing Editor for Lotus Library: Julie Gale Watson
Developmental Editor: Jennifer Watson Ervedosa
Cover design and typesetting by www.clareconnieshepherd.com

Lotus Library is an imprint of Watson Caring Science Institute,
a 501C(3) international non-profit foundation.

Watson Caring Science Institute,
4450 Arapahoe Avenue Suite 100,
Boulder, CO 80303,
USA
www.watsoncaringscience.org

Acknowledgements

With deepest love and gratitude I would like to thank:
Dr. Jean Watson for her loving kindness, wisdom and
inspiration and for having faith in me. Sarah Hough for sharing
her gift, her sensitivity, support and precious friendship.
Julie and Jennifer Watson for their gentle guidance and encouragement
in writing this book and all the extraordinary women who continue
to be part of the story. You offer dreams to live again.

The Caritas community, for holding light, especially Dr Gayle Casterline,
Dr Marcia Hills, Dr Sara Horton-Deutsch, Dr Lynne Wagner
and all those who have walked alongside.

Maggie and Barbara for holding the fort and keeping
me laughing for 32 years.

Matthew-Jack and James Francis, for your blessing and for
being just who you are. I love you more than words can say.

Dedication

For Fran

'Still here, there and everywhere in

this pandimensional universe'

(Todaro-Franceschi, 2006)

Foreword

Jean Watson

Anna Biley offers us a path through wild nature: mindful dying processes, uncovering mysteries, micro-miracles of insights as metaphors of the sacred circle of life/death as one unitary field. It is the sonnets of soul that are revealed whole in this work, as change and transformation of self occurs between these pages. This new space, where the 'birds hold secrets,' ushers the reader into a space where death becomes the greatest teacher of both living and remembering.

In this book Anna Biley also has offered us another world of science, philosophy, art and humanity, within the context of Unitary Caring Science. Through her original and creative methodological scholarship of autoethnography, this work evolved from Anna's academic dissertation, and it brings to life a deep offering from self to the discipline and profession of nursing, in need of "remembering" its purpose. In applying an innovative, postmodern cut up poetry technique, Biley captures the intense phenomenon she is personally undergoing and enduring and allows new meaning to emerge from the systematic collection of all of her data. This approach serves as a living metaphor, mirroring and mimicking the anguish, beauty, depth and unpredictable, 'cut-up,' non-linear nature of inner and outer experiences of grief, conscious dying, love and remembering. This book also can be seen as a book on Conscious Dying, revealing tragedy and struggles as Anna lived, despaired and loved as she cared for Fran; her devoted, brilliant scholar, artistic and eccentric husband.

Fran was an enigma. I knew him for many years through shared values and unitary science philosophies, scholarship, and international conferences in England and Germany. Fran always surprised and interrupted mainstream thinking and mainstream mindsets, whether in science, academe, or in life itself. For some reason, Fran always reminded me of the gifted Welsh actor, Richard Burton; Fran, another

Welshman, and depth-actor of life, stalked the other side of life, deep down to the core; sometimes shocking, always waking up those in his midst. Fran, academically renowned, intensely lived out his pandimensional philosophies and occupied them head-long, face-to-face, with all the vicissitudes of: living/changing/challenging/learning/growing/Being-Becoming.

Anna offers a "Personal Remembering," which transcends science and self and invites the reader into the unitary field of human existence-nonexistence, in harmony, and one with nature, life cycles, environment and the cosmos. Finally, within the unitary field in which Fran and Anna dwelled, the veil is very thin. Enter this work as an experience into the pandimensional artistic universe of Anna's Caritas-love, grief and remembering, with beauty-all-around.

Birds hold our secrets...

Remembering purpose is how a broken heart heals.
The sensation is like resilience, strength and patience,
shaking memory. Stay awake,
unfolding moments witness,
walking alongside is what you are here to do.
Unitary consciousness, like remembering purpose,
will be sensitive to cultivating patience.

Human Caring Science must be lived,
in walking alongside in caring, healing love
and light
there is sad peace.

Ways of being, a deep knowing and intuition
of poetry, ethically disciplined behaviour, loving
kindness,
became remembering purpose.
Re-arranging, re-patterning time and mind
remembering purpose.
Women who are extraordinary offer the gift of dreams
to awaken care, love, intention.

Mother becoming consciousness.
Be still. Allow what you know to come to the fore.
Walking alongside, wash suffering,
take small steps,
it is the same path of tears, hope and joy.

Re-patterning birth,
inner knowing, intimacy and comfort,
sacred feminine, strength and mystery in purpose.
All is connected in the labyrinth,
memories, mindful touch, transcended pain,
simple humanity, compassion, silent dignity,
caring presence.
Nursing transformed into living purpose.
Ancient remembering.

Author's Foreword

It could be argued that of all professions, nursing is the one with which caring is most associated. Nursing is a caring profession, right? Yes! But why then are hospital complaints on the rise and failures of care reported daily in the British media, constantly the subject of debate in Parliament (Aynsley-Green, 2018). Why are nurses leaving the profession and recruitment numbers struggling? (Kendall-Raynor, 2018). Of course the reasons are complex, but could it be suggested that for many nurses the capacity to care is increasingly diminished in a system starved of resources, thus exposing the unbearable truth that perhaps, intention to care and reality are incongruent? And where does that leave the individual nurse when efforts in the workplace are constantly undermined, and the capacity to care for self even more so? Enter nursing theorist and philosopher, Jean Watson.

Watson first introduced her Theory of Human Caring in 1979, and for over forty years, this work has been honed and developed, to become what is now known as Unitary Caring Science (Watson, 2018). This work is gathering momentum on a global scale and it has an ever-increasing research base, models of education and practice to support it (Horton-Deutsch and Anderson, 2018; Rosa, Horton-Deutsch and Watson 2018). Unitary Caring Science is philosophical, theoretical and some may say, almost spiritual in nature. It proudly upholds disciplinary values, morals and ethics, and it gives voice to a language of caring. Unitary Caring Science speaks to and touches people's lived experience and quite simply, makes sense. In a world where policy, procedure, and corporate demands often take priority over need, it challenges us to reconnect with what it means to be human and face it, in all its beauty, mess and broken-ness, and in doing so, to face our own vulnerability and potential for healing.

Every small act has an impact on the wider environment, and humanity is increasingly challenged to awaken to the reality that we live in a world, a quantum universe, where everything is connected and everything matters. It is worthy of note that it was Florence Nightingale who first stated that the role of the nurse is to put the patient in the best environment for nature to act (Nightingale, 1859/2010). In the context of Unitary Caring Science, Watson suggests that all relationships are transpersonal, meaning that they work all ways, human to human, and that is how it should be (Watson, 2018). We will never truly know the effect we have on others and which moments make a difference, but based on the assumption that everyone and everything is connected, then everything and every moment has the potential to be a moment of caring.

Remembering who we are as a discipline is a moral imperative for nursing and is a vital quest that humanity requires of the profession (Watson, 2018). What it means to be human is the business of nursing and through a disciplinary lens of caring and healing; Unitary Caring Science is an invitation to explore values, philosophies and ethics that reflect this. It offers us the creative space to delve into the most intimate of human experiences such as: birth, death, joy, loss and remembering purpose; to formulate new research methods and modes of enquiry, to offer fresh insight and understanding of who we are and why we are here, and to support an evolving unitary world order in which human consciousness and the moral stance of belonging is key to a viable future (Newman, 2008; Reeder, 2013).

What follows is my personal story that grew in part from my doctorate research study at the Watson Caring Science Institute, carried out in 2014. The chosen methodology for this research was autoethnography, 'a distinct research approach to the study of human experience' (Denzin, 2014, p. 7), in which the researcher is also the research subject. Placing the self in a specific cultural context, autoethnography requires the researcher to simultaneously take a wide-angled and reflexive lens and a deep dive into self (Ellis & Bochner, 2000), zooming in and out, recognising and remembering pattern.

And so I placed a vulnerable self in the culture of Unitary Caring Science, caring values and ethics, with the caritas processes ® inviting an exploration of how loving kindness, mindful intention, intuition, authenticity, compassion and dignity were manifest in moments of caring, relationship and remembering. It is important to note that autoethnography is a research methodology. What distinguishes it from simply a narrative or reflective account is the systematic analysis, synthesis and crafting of data, and that it has an ethical basis. The raw research data was made up of journal entries, emails, literature, music, songs, poetry and art, layered and folded into the text, deepening and widening the story. On completion, a post-modern cut-up poetry technique was used (Biley, 1998, 2004, 2016) to further dwell with the story, inviting new meaning to emerge. Open to beauty, art and the unknown Unitary Caring Science was the framework for an innovative research process that was experienced not analysed (Biley, 2004), and that yielded findings poetic and metaphorical rather than literal (Watson, 2012).

Introduction

Somewhere out at the edges, the night is turning and the waves of darkness begin to brighten the shore of dawn. The heavy dark falls back to earth and the freed air goes wild with light. The heart fills with fresh, bright breath and thoughts stir to give birth to colour.
(O'Donohue, 2000, p. xiii)

This is a story of love and remembering. It is not a self help book (there are enough of those), nor will it tell you what to expect or give you any learning outcomes. Rather it is an invitation to walk alongside and share a simple story. Maybe it will touch you, speak to you or help you resolve something, or perhaps it will pop into your head sometime in the future as you meet similar challenges in nursing practice or when the death of a loved one comes knocking at your door.

My husband Fran died of cancer at the age of 54. Fran was a mental health nurse and academic but his proudest achievement was being a dad. Ours was a complex and convoluted relationship and far from perfect but as nurses, it was a love of our profession that drew us together and throughout our relationship of 23 years we were each other's nurse, companion and soul mate. The day my love was diagnosed with cancer a part of me died. Fran was also a wood turner and sculptor and as a man with a shed, liked nothing more than pottering around making things such as wooden bowls, spoons, garden ornaments and on one occasion, even another shed! Our 300-year old, clapped out house was cluttered with his creations and half finished projects. I used to roll my eyes and tut, as every weekend more was added to the bulging bookcases and dining table. He used to tease; "You will appreciate it when I am gone." One thing about Fran, he was always right. One day he asked for my help, to hold a ladder whilst he climbed up into a tree and nailed up a plaque that he had just made from an old, reclaimed plank of oak, the letters burned into the wood read, birds hold our secrets. The title of this book not only acknowledges that quintessentially Fran eccentric day, but became a metaphor, as I found myself walking alongside, holding the ladder and keeping the balance as he lived his dying.

Over time I have observed how people move in and out of the circle of grief. New, unexpected people emerge, as others forget and move on with their own lives. Some stay, quietly walking alongside, ever ready to support, comfort, and catch you gently when the pain is too much. I am blessed with such a friend in Sarah Hough. A gifted artist, I asked Sarah if she would kindly draw a picture of the garden and little woodland alongside our house as a keepsake. One picture, discussed over a cup of tea in the kitchen, became a series of pictures and a year-long creative project which ultimately came to support my doctoral dissertation and this book. We walked around the little woodland, observing the changing seasons, the birds and the quirky bits and pieces scattered around the place: the sculptures, the shed and an old dairy churn. We spoke about the hawthorn, foxgloves, the fire pit, the owl box, the cherry blossom in Spring, and berries in the Winter. And as we dwelt in that space, we also noticed how Fran's work had started to breakdown, to decay and return to nature; being reabsorbed back into the woodland landscape. The seasons of the woodland became a metaphor for life and like grief, it is forever changing and forever new. Sarah's gift to me was to capture the transformative 'unitary rhythm of dying-grieving' (Malinski, 2012, p. 239), as well as the quintessential Fran, and in doing so, she has created something fresh, breathing new life and meaning into something extraordinary.

History is peppered with legend and metaphors of transformative episodes and it is not unusual to want to honour a loved one, perhaps through a creative tribute, a memorial or an activity such as fundraising for a charity. Some may say that this is merely an emotional response to stress, no more than a result of 'products of the brain and its neurotransmitters' (Wein, 2014, p. 92), an innate human need to explain death. On one level this is not surprising. After all, we live in a modern society where death, frailty and vulnerability are simply embarrassing, almost irrelevant, and where extreme emotional responses can be diagnosed, treated and quashed. How sad. As a nurse, wife, daughter and sister I have learned that the dying are our greatest teachers and that being alongside can be life transforming and life enhancing, a catalyst for awakening to what makes us human, to compassion, self awareness and wisdom. When

Fran was diagnosed he said, "Well, if we have to do this we are going to do it mindfully," and we consciously set that intention. But what did he mean by that, and how is that even possible in the dark, scary rawness and uncertainty that comes with dying? In discussing grief and loss, the spiritual teacher Ram Dass stated, 'Let's say you're in "wise-woman training". Everything in life must be grist for the mill. The relationship with this man would become part of the wisdom in you.' (Dass, n.d. para. 6).

Virginia Woolf wrote, "I meant to write about death only life came breaking in as usual" (1922/1981, p. 167). In the final few weeks I had with Fran, I came to know that everything that had gone before was part of the now, mere preparation to be in each moment with him. As two nurses, the experiences and influences that came before brought us to that moment when Fran came to live his dying in mindfulness. What we lived then has unfolded, becoming the future, which is the now. Of course Fran is no longer here to tell his story but I am in a unique position to be able to draw on his academic and published work to tell mine. His was an avant-garde character, who lived life to the full and I know he would embrace it. He was never afraid to challenge or provoke discomfort in seeking new ways of knowing, but would equally embody my intention of loving kindness.

When relationships are woven together in the rich tapestry of life and its transitions, each individual, be they dying or caring, has their own purpose to remember, their own path to follow, treading carefully to avoid the potential danger of the other's fear, need or ego unintentionally encroaching on the other. This is my story, of how we lived the 92 days from Fran's diagnosis to death, how I survived the grief and loneliness beyond, how I came to remember purpose and to trust my deepest intuition. The connection between dying and birth was a constant thread of personal remembering. Somehow, I knew what to do because I had done it before.

Chapter 1

What we call the beginning is often the end. And to make an end is to make a beginning. The end is where we start from. (T. S. Eliot 1944/1959, p. 47)

Writing for me has always been a way out and a way in. For as long as I can remember I have written things down. I am a maker of lists and a keeper of notes, always made with the same intention: to capture gems of information, jewels of poetry and random trinkets of meaning for later use from stories and literature. As a child my treasures were kept in a small wooden box with my name carved messily in blue pen on the lid, with a warning to all – Private: Keep out! Now as a grown-up, I have very few personal possessions of any real value to myself, except for a hoard of little notebooks and files, along with the odd letter and latterly, handmade cards and drawings made by my children. I cannot recall what happened to the little box, but as I reflect on my journals past and present, I can see that spirituality, soul, peace and caring have been constant threads of awareness and curiosity for me over the past 50 years. Narrative and poetry of mindfulness and conscious dying, the random jigsaw pieces, connecting across time, to create a picture of a personal, lived experience, which I have come to name remembering purpose. Over the years, my journal has created the space in which I continue to allow thoughts and feelings to manifest, 'allowing my soul/soulful purpose to catch up' (Watson, 2005, p. 141).

My early childhood world began at a park, with beds of pink roses and winding sandy paths, and ended at a fork in the road where there was a red post box hidden among the layers of a dry stone wall. We lived in an 'old lady' street, bordered to the North and East by the untamed Yorkshire moors and to the West, the haunting and austere Pennine hills of Lancashire, the witching county. As a family we were raised to have a love of reading and a thirst for knowledge. For our parents, as working-class children in the Second World War, there was little prospect of education beyond the age of fourteen and so, as if to make up for lost time, they filled our home with books: musty, secondhand children's stories, classics and collections of encyclopedias, some of them dating back to the 1930s. Visits to the public library were a regular treat and some of my earliest memories are of my mother sitting between me and my brother, an arm round each of us, reading stories of *The faraway tree* and *The muddleheaded wombat*, from dog-eared, acrid smelling books.

My grandmother too was a storyteller and poet but her tales and rhymes came from her own thoughts. In 1917, at the age of 12, she was forced to leave school and begin part-time work as a weaver in one of the town's cotton mills, alongside her mother and sisters. She was not blessed with education and opportunity but with her northern common sense, big heart and innate capacity to love, she became the local woman who delivered the babies and laid out the dead. My grandmother lived in a flat above the hairdresser's shop, six doors down from where I was born. Much to my delight and my brother's disgust, if we held hands and stayed together, we were allowed to visit her on our own. And so most afternoons we would burst through the door and scramble on to her ample lap. So vivid were her images that we really did believe that Noddy lived in our street and would come to play one day. Alas we rarely heard the end of the story. Suspended by the rhythm of her clapped-out rocking chair and the drone of whirling hair dryers muffling the cackle of women below, we dozed into our afternoon nap. Those sticky, sickly hairspray smelling days spent at my grandmother's house are sealed in consciousness and time and are the happy, safe memories of early childhood.

At the age of 4, I distinctly remember the unbridled joy of unlocking the mystery when I read my first word, Look! This unfortunately was coupled by my frustration at starting school, and being told that I was too young to read! As I grew, books and stories became my greatest love and in the absence of teen fiction, authors such as Enid Blyton, Agatha Christie, Jane Austen, Charlotte, Emily and Anne Brontë, Virginia Woolf and Thomas Hardy were some of the greatest influences in the early years. For as long as I can remember, books have been the precious key, an invitation to explore, a way out and a way in. I have never been alone, nor am I scared of my own company. I have my books. Recently, whilst watching the film *The history boys*, I was reminded of the excitement and joy that only reading brings, as a schoolmaster, played by the remarkable

Richard Griffiths recalls:

> The best moments in reading are when you come across
> something, a thought, a feeling, a way of looking at a thing you
> thought particular, special to you. And here it is. Set down by
> someone, a person you have never met, sometimes long dead. It
> is as if a hand has come out and taken yours. (Bennett, 2004).

With Irish ancestry, mine was a Roman Catholic world, a
community in which God and religion were never very far away.
Without exception, fear and demons ruled. I was told that my
problem, my sin, was that I had too much imagination, that I asked
too many questions and that it was about time I realised that life was
not a fairytale. I was 8 years old. Terrified of priests, nuns and adults
in general, the only safe place was in my head, where fear could be
diluted occasionally with the clandestine comfort of believing in
miracles, angels and music.

As a good Catholic teenager in the 1970s, a love of reading and the
desire to explore a wider spirituality led to the teachings of Mother
Teresa and John Paul II, and of course to the Gospels and New
Testament. Inevitably the oxymoronic state of adolescence meant that
my search was driven both by a desire to fit in and to break free of the
Catholic world I knew. Over time, an inherent, child-like devotion
to Mary the Mother of God blossomed into a wider appreciation
of the sacred feminine, an unfolding awareness of the power of
gentleness, kindness and the gift of spirit in nature, an evolving
consciousness that continues to bring me joy and understanding. As
a young woman, my longing to truly live the Gospels, led to 10 years
of voluntary carer work with disabled children's charities, and to the
work of Jean Vanier, a Catholic layman and founder of the global
L'Arche movement. Living in community, with men and women with
learning disabilities, Vanier wrote of compassion, healing and service,
of common humanity and journeying to the heart (Vanier, 1979,
1997), all themes that have continued to reverberate with me over the
years. Moving farther and farther away from structured religion, the
Catholic social peace and justice movement of the 1980s continued
to shape my thinking and belief that actions speak louder than words
and that simple humanity, compassion and walking alongside the

vulnerable must be lived if it is to mean anything at all. This urgent, burning passion and delicate, fragile awakening, I now witness in my sons. Across time, as the ultimate existential questions resonate – who are you? What brings you here? – I want to tell them that all is well, that destiny has been sowing her seeds since before they were born. Let go. Let it be.

A keeper of notes unlocking the mystery, teachings,
secretly connecting across time.
Teenage, Catholic rhymes, trinkets of words,
blended a story of a soul journey,
healing and service.
Remembering purpose threads
humanity, caring, sacred feminine,
a longing to truly live.

Of the books I have ever read, the one that changed my life most profoundly came to me at the age of 20 in 1983. The autobiography of a young volunteer nurse in the First World War, *Testament of youth* is the story of Vera Brittain. The heart-wrenching narrative of love, loss, care, compassion, postwar feminism and peace activism; this book directly led to my decision to become a nurse. Thirty years later, in pondering just how and why this book had such an impact, I took it down from the shelf and remembered:

In 1914 as a middle-class Edwardian young lady, destined for Oxford University, Vera witnessed her fiancé, brother and closest friends signing up to the army and going to war in France. Unable to stand by 'as life looks out from the scene of human struggle with the awful face of duty' (Brittain, 1933/1978, p. 98), Vera signed up as a Red Cross VAD nurse (Voluntary Aid Detachment) in 1915. 'To become a nurse was my intention,' (p. 146). 'The place now of anyone who is young and strong and capable is where the work that is needed is to be done' (p. 214). Standing alongside and becoming the voice of a generation, Vera Brittain served as a nurse throughout the duration of the First World War. Recalling that 'there was hardly an intimate service I did not perform' (p. 165), Vera wrote detailed and graphic accounts of injury, pain, devastation and death; of, 'fleshless blackened bones of simple men who poured out their red sweet wine of youth,' (p. 198). As a then 20 year old, I remember how inspired I was by the passion, dedication, skill, efficiency and sheer hard work of nursing that is described in *Testament of youth*. Of commitment in standing alongside and making a difference, but moreover I was moved by the gentleness, compassion and 'gratitude' (p. 166) of service and of empathy. For example, when caring for German soldiers, Vera reflects that, 'someone loves the man lying there,' (p. 138). Had it been a story of macho heroes, triumph and victory in the classic sense, the impact may not have been so significant on me. As events unfolded, the morals and ethics of war illustrate the unbearable struggle of that generation. The author reflects: 'It is quite impossible to understand how we can be such strong individualists, so insistent on the rights and claims of every human soul, and yet, at the same time countenance this wholesale murder' (p. 175). This is poignantly illustrated in a letter from her fiancé, who wrote, 'Bees are in the clover that overhang the trench, it is a pity to kill people on a day like this,' (p. 196). As the allure of war was replaced by cynicism and suspicion, Vera lived the paradox of an increasing conviction in the futility of war, whilst witnessing unparalleled strength and stoicism and questioned, 'Who can say that victory is worth the death of even one of these?' (p. 198). Reading *Testament of youth* again, older and wiser, is like looking through the same kaleidoscope and experiencing a distinct shift in pattern, focus and colour. With maturity and time, the universal human experience of grief and loss resonates even more, and Vera's drive to find new meaning and purpose against a backdrop of feminism and finding voice is a familiar echo. She knew who she was.

Later that same year, I had my first real life encounter with death. Not much more than a child myself, I got a job in a Catholic children's home and was overwhelmingly out of my depth in dealing with the complex, disturbed lives of the youngsters there. My role was generic in that I was the cleaner, shopper, kitchen assistant and carer. I became particularly close to one young man, Liam. He was sixteen and had learning difficulties. He was the misfit in the home and was often bullied by the children and staff alike. One Christmas, upon returning from a stay with relatives, he became ill and was admitted to the hospital where he was diagnosed with peritonitis. He died a month later.

During Liam's days in intensive care I took my turn sitting with him, sometimes throughout the night, and as I sat, I watched the nurses as they went about their business, administering loving care and kindness to the dying child in front of me. It was about 4:00am one Sunday morning when a nurse came to the bedside. Witnessing her speak to Liam, wipe his face and hands, adjust his catheter and administer mouth care, was one of the most profound experiences of loving kindness I have ever seen and I knew that something extraordinary was happening. From that moment, in my nursing practice and in life, that encounter has remained a benchmark, illustrating Florence Nightingale's stance that 'the very elements of nursing are all but unknown' (Nightingale, 1859/2010, p. 6). A paradox of simplicity and mystery, in remembering that moment, I remember purpose. At worst arrogant and at best naive, in my cloistered Catholic world, I knew only about values and ethics from a religious perspective. Witnessing Liam's nursing care I began to awaken to the beauty of humanity and saw a new world view of healthcare that, although far from perfect, was full of people with good intention, not for some eternal reward but because it is morally and ethically the right thing to do and quite simply, it is what makes us human.

The dying child
mystery, care and kindness, experienced
overwhelmingly in front of me.
Witnessing her speak, administering love,
the simplicity. Profound.

Chapter 2

Waiting and becoming is the symbolic meaning of being 'called to ordination,'
allowing the Divine to awaken part of your spirit that contains the essence
of what you are capable of contributing to others as well as self.
(Gibran, 1995, p. 254)

Everything began to make sense when I came home to nursing.
Sensing purpose and starting to awaken to understanding why I am
here, was both exciting and alarming and as ever, life remained full
of irony and contradictions. In many ways I remember my life as a
student nurse, and in the early years after qualifying, as happy times
sharing the joys and sorrows of nursing with colleagues and friends,
and of meeting extraordinary role models whose names, faces and
caring actions, I remember to this day. On one such occasion I was
called upon to attend to a dead body, also known as the procedure of
'last offices' or 'laying out'. In the 1980s it was nursing school policy
for students to demonstrate this as an early learning outcome and
so I was sent to an unfamiliar ward, to care for a young patient who
had collapsed and died on admission to the hospital. Terrified, I was
met and supported by a kind and gentle nurse, who, with warmth and
understanding, talked to me as we removed the dead woman's dirty,
vomit-stained clothes. Washing the body of a stranger, her mottled
hands, her waxy appearing breasts and marble face, brushing her
thick, shiny hair and wrapping her in clean sheets was a sacred act.
As the nurse placed a fresh pink rose on the woman's chest, I knew, as
with Liam, that I was witnessing something special and that this was
the kind of nurse I wanted to be. Indeed many years later I wrote of
this and other encounters: of sacred caring moments, of intuition and
simple humanity; as nurses uphold the dignity of the vulnerable, the
dying and the dead (Biley, 1997, 2000).

The bond between nurses can be extraordinary. The men and
women who share the experience of life, death, pain, suffering; the
delight of recovery, the love of families. Nurses are those who sit with
the marginalised and wash the broken and because of this, they have

a unique ability to understand and to hold each other in helpless laughter and through tears of frustration and despair.

However, these deepest of human connections were juxtaposed with moments of isolation and loneliness as I struggled to understand the absence of love and compassion I also often experienced, in the profession that I adored. I pondered why nurses did not talk about caring and love, why it was not included in the curriculum and why so many encounters with patients lacked the compassion and empathy I had witnessed at Liam's bedside. The conspiracy of silence when it came to caring was deafening and the shame of admitting to feelings of connection and compassion, palpable. Again I poured out my soul in my journal and delved into literature, searching for likeminded connections. Reading a biography of Florence Nightingale, her sense of nursing as an art and spiritual practice resonated with me (Woodham-Smith, 1955), and to this day, *Notes on nursing*, written 160 years ago, quite simply makes sense in it's wisdom, realism, common sense and good humour. Indeed now, as the parent of teenagers, I recently jokingly quoted Nightingale's observation that, 'Bedrooms are almost universally foul. Do you ever go into the bedroom of any person of any class and find the air anything but unwholesomely close and foul?' (Nightingale, 1859/2010, p. 11).

However, it was in discovering the work of Jean Watson, an American nursing theorist, that I truly began to feel that I was not alone (Watson, 1988). As a young woman of 25, Watson's stance, that nursing is first and foremost about human connection, resonated, and like a homing beacon, I set out to learn more. In due course, I was proud and honoured to qualify as a registered nurse (RN), and I took up a staff nurse post in a rehabilitation unit in the North of England, where I was promoted to ward manager within a year. A thirst for knowledge instinctively led me to books and I was inspired by the idea of primary nursing, a system whereby patients had one main nurse throughout a hospital stay. It was argued that providing this continuity improved the quality and experience of care, possibly leading to faster discharge and reduced readmission rates (Manthey, 1980; Wright, 1994). Specific nursing development units were established to test out this and other innovations and the emerging trend towards nurses as reflective practitioners meant that the late 1980s and early 1990s was a period of creativity and change in British nursing. And I totally embraced it, regularly attending study days and conferences, listening and talking to inspirational nurse leaders who were the drivers of change, not only at the practice level but who were also helping to shape the government policy of the day.

Keen to explore how our little clinical team could adopt some of these changes, I arranged for the hospital's nursing development facilitator to help us with some training. It was at that point that Francis Biley came into my life. To my surprise and our amusement, we found ourselves at the epicentre of canteen gossip and in spite of advice to the contrary, the longhaired, cigarette smoking, atheist hippie stayed alongside the nice Catholic girl for 23 years. Always an avant-garde character, Fran was known for his challenging and innovative approach to life and to nursing practice. A small framed, thin man with mousey coloured hair, he wasn't the hunky rugby playing type that I usually fell for, but fall for him I did and from the moment we met, we shared a burning love for nursing and connected at every level. An undated journal entry reminds me of that time:

> It is wrong to think that love comes from long
> companionship and persevering courtship. Love is the
> off spring of spiritual affinity and unless that affinity is
> created in a moment, it will not be created in years or even
> generations (Gibran, 1995, p. 149).

Setting the pace, within the first year Fran swept me off to travel in India and we relocated to South Wales, so that he could pursue an academic career and doctoral studies. I continued nursing and doing occasional classroom clinical tuition whilst also studying for a Masters degree. Ten years passed from starting nurse training to eventually meeting Jean Watson at Oxford University in 1994. A year later, inspired by her talk on Human Caring Science, I received a scholarship from the Florence Nightingale Foundation in London. At the age of 32 and twenty weeks pregnant with our first child, I set off alone, across the Atlantic Ocean, to study for the certificate in caring praxis at the then Center for Human Caring in Denver, Colorado.

As nursing has evolved as a discipline, it has developed the confidence and competence to challenge the traditional medical models of practice, whereby the person is reduced to a physical entity,

29

separate from mind, spirit and soul, and where the curing rather than caring paradigm is dominant (Watson, 1995). Whilst respecting traditional approaches, Caring Science offers a unitary world view and an 'ethical, philosophical and moral disciplinary foundation ... for value-centered 21st century nursing' (Watson, 2012, p. 18). Caring Science is grounded in the ethics and values of belonging as described by the 20th-century philosopher Emmanuel Levinas:

> Ethics is the first principle for science and an 'Ethic of Belonging' (to the infinite cosmic field of universal love) is the starting point for our world view and comes before our notion of each of us as separate from this larger cosmos and from each other (Watson, 2012, p. 21).

Distinct from, but complementary to medicine, Caring Science honours and values the uniqueness and oneness of the unitary human being. Nurses are co-participants in an unfolding journey of being with the other, with caring intention and trust, as both find their own meaning and purpose. Central to this perspective is the human relationship, with the nurture and care of self (nurse) in a mutual, evolving connection. The values of Caring Science are encapsulated in the caritas processes ® and may be summarised as:

10 CARITAS PROCESSES ®

- Practicing loving kindness/compassion and peace with self/other.

- Being authentically present, enabling faith/hope/ belief system and subjective world of self/other.

- Being sensitive to self/others by cultivating own spiritual practice.

- Developing and sustaining loving, trusting, caring relationships.

- Allowing for the expression of feelings, authentically listening and holding anothers story.

- Creative problem–solving, through all ways of knowing/doing/being.

- Authentic teaching-learning within the context of caring relationships.

- Creating a healing environment at all levels, embracing consciousness, wholeness, beauty, dignity and peace.

- Holding intention, dignity and caring consciousness in the sacred acts of bodily care.

- Opening to mystery and existential dimensions, allowing for miracles (Watson, 2008).

In the human relationship, the caritas processes may be made manifest in the transpersonal, caring moment. Acting with compassion, kindness and mindful, intentional, caring presence, the authentic caring moment is a connection of souls and a manifestation of oneness (Watson, 1999, 2005). Indeed it could be argued that the caritas processes are a natural, human response and an ethical and moral expression of appreciating the human (self and other) as embodied soul and spirit. Furthermore, from personal, lived experience, it may be suggested that Being in caring consciousness is also a journey of Becoming and that some transpersonal relationships and caring moments break through to a deeper level of consciousness and oneness with the universe.

In contrast to the traditional, empirical epistemology of the medical model, Caring Science requires an ontological perspective, with the overarching quest being to find out 'what it means to be human' (Watson, 2012, p. 24). Caring Science does not limit knowledge development to the physical, as we know it, but creates space to embrace the unknown, to reflect and contemplate (Watson, 2005).

Studying in Denver was life transforming for me, and what began to unfold then, has become integral to every aspect of life since. Holding the beautifully handwritten notes, so preciously preserved from that time, I remember, reflect and understand how much has seeped into consciousness and has become a way of being – the values of human care, transpersonal, caring relationships, the caritas processes (Watson, 1988) and the moral imperative to do the right thing. One of my journal entries from that time reads: 'make no judgments, have no expectations. Give up the need to know why things happen as they do. Trust unscheduled events = spiritual direction.'

For the first time it was possible to talk about caring, spirituality and even love in nursing, without shame and embarrassment. During my month in Denver, reading remained a source of strength and delight, as I immersed myself in caring theory. Grateful for the introduction to the poet Rainer Maria Rilke (1934/1993), I reflect on his *Letters to a young poet* and still find his words both comforting and reassuring:

Of all my books just a few are indispensable to me...
Live a while in these books, learn from them what seems
to you worth learning but above all, love them. This love
will be repaid to you a thousand and a thousand times,
and however your life may turn, it will, I am certain of
it, run through the fabric of your growth as one of the
most important threads among all the threads of your
experiences, disappointments and joys (p. 25).

Becoming acquainted with the work of the Jewish philosopher
Viktor Frankel, contributed significantly to my later M. Sc work,
in which I explore the search for soul, purpose and meaning as a
human response to suffering (Frankel, 1946/1984, 2012). Being
introduced to Native American wisdom and spirituality was also
inspiring, as I listened and learned about our Mother the Earth and
of stillness, patience and listening, as one walks the sacred path (Black
Elk & Lyon, 1990). On leaving Denver in the summer of 1995, I
soon became a full-time mum, and completed a M. Sc in nursing
in snatched moments as I fed my baby through the night. Clinical
practice became part-time night duty, supplemented with occasional
freelance lecturing. But more importantly, my intention was to
approach nursing practice and life in a new way, living caring values,
grateful that my soul searching and love of literature and poetry made
sense and had found a home in the context of human Caring Science.
It was as if everything had been leading to this.

Philosopher, I sat by Fran's bedside.
caring theory, spreading out roots,
a source of strength and patience. Destiny,
sowing seeds.
Immersed in the poet
I explored Being as sacred path.

Chapter 3

Instead of a fabric, I hold in my hands a bundle of a thousand knotted threads, which would occupy hundreds of hands for years to disentangle and straighten out, even if every thread did not become terribly brittle and break between the fingers as soon as it is handled and gently teased out.
(Hesse, 1956/1995, p. 38)

And then it all went wrong and I honestly wondered if I had become too comfortable (or too smug), in this world of caring intention. Whatever the reason, it was the first reminder of the pain and cost of living caritas and was a lesson that I would draw on many times, not least of all in the depths of loss. Something happened which led me to doubt caring theory, nursing practice and my whole existence in the world. I was stalked and threatened by a man whose elderly mother I had cared for whilst she was dying. Guilt ridden, it was easy to believe the cruel inner echo that at best I was stupid and naive, and at worst, I asked for it. It was deserved. Our home violated and my relationship with Fran under extreme duress, it was clear that my caring intentions had backfired and as my whole world fell apart, I wrote in my journal:

> Caring. What the hell does that mean? Risk taking you
> say? Pain I say. Care and it all comes back in your face.
> Take, that's what people want. Like bloody parasites, take,
> take, take. They'll bleed you till you are dry and then come
> back for more. To kick you when you are down, 'More,
> more, more' they scream, until your head is spinning. You
> feel sick, you can't sleep, but still they come. Knocking
> at your door, hiding in corners to jump out at you when
> you least expect it. I need care, to be held and cherished. I
> need to sleep peacefully in my bed and awake to feel the
> warm sun, on my face, in my soul. But what do you care?
> Transpersonal shit. So long as I am there to 'care' you will take
> (Biley & Giovannoni, 2018, p. 141).

"Grief is our companion, showing up in the strangest places," (Bowman, 1994, p.2). Losing the dream of how our home, relationship and family life would unfold was devastating. Basing my practice on caring theory, my plan was to become a reflexologist, but this dream in tatters was never to be resurrected. Nevertheless I was determined that my abuser would not steal my inner self and that I must remember my values and not sink into a vortex of darkness and cruelty. Searching for understanding, I turned to the Buddhist teachings of the Dalai Lama and found that his wisdom and ethics on cultivating patience and healing anger was the key to keeping soul, spirit and caring values alive; a key to remembering purpose. Noting that, 'ethics are a necessary means to ensure we do not harm each other' (Dalai Lama, 1999, p. 66), my journal reads, 'Those who harm us are in a sense our teachers (of patience). They give us unparalleled opportunities to practise ethically disciplined behaviour,' (p. 114). Furthermore, 'Suffering has good qualities. Through being disheartened with it, arrogance is dispelled, compassion arises, evil is shunned and joy is found in virtue' (Dalai Lama, 1997, p. 38). Had I really been too smug or too comfortable, or had I missed something? In thinking I was nurturing helping, trusting, caring relationships, I had failed to be sensitive to my own vulnerability. Sitting with the old lady as she passed peacefully, I was so deeply involved in that caring occasion, I had not seen the danger signs, that her son was becoming increasingly obsessed with my every move and every aspect of my life. With intention I tried to absorb the teaching that 'those who wish to cause me suffering are like Buddha's bestowing waves of blessing … why should I be angry with them' (Dalai Lama, 1997, p. 94). But it was difficult. Oh so difficult, and actually beyond my capacity at the time. Although an innate belief in kindness and right relationships was unshaken, I was wounded and have never been quite the same. Even now, I am more reserved, shyer, quieter and less confident and it has taken many years to feel safe again. It changed me. But, over time, life experience has taught me that grief brings out the best and the worst in people and if we are to uphold ethically disciplined values and caring principles we must face and see the humanity in others (Watson, 2018). However 'this should not be interpreted as excusing an individual's offending behaviour or their responsibility to take accountability for their actions' (Biley & Giovannoni, 2018,

p. 144). Whilst it can heal and deepen love, grief may also awaken jealousy, greed, fear, unresolved anger and old family resentments. On reflection I now acknowledge the experience for what it was: the complicated grief of the perpetrator. For me, an opportunity to deepen self-knowledge, a reality check in which I learned that true caritas can be raw and painful. At best an awakening, a new echo of remembering purpose that reverberates in the now, in loss and grief.

Be sensitive to cultivating patience, awakening care, love
ethically disciplined behaviour.
Losing the dream, was devastating
then I see joy is found in the patience of living caritas.
Wounded, in tatters, purpose determined that I reach out.
wisdom and ethics, somehow the key to ensure caring values,
My own vulnerability a teacher.

Chapter 4

*For one human being to love another: that is perhaps the most difficult of
all our tasks, the ultimate, the last test and proof, the work for which all
other work is but preparation. (Rilke, 1934/1993, p. 54)*

A chapter published in *A Handbook for caring science* (2018)
describes how:

> In 2012, life invited me to live Caring Science at a deeper
> and more personal level than I ever thought was possible,
> as I cared for my lovely Fran. Embracing human caring
> and living the caritas processes® took me to the brink
> of excruciating pain and profound peace, a paradox of
> heartfelt moments, of love and light, of messy, painful,
> lonely days. Being truly present and holding caring
> intention in reality often meant absorbing hurt, frustration
> and sadness. Frequently, the 'self' as described in the caritas
> processes (Watson, 2008) was invisible, as the world
> seemed to be asking more of me than I could ever give.
> (Biley, 2018, p. 633)

In the book *Grace and grit*, Ken Wilber (1993), shares the story
of Treya his wife, and their journey with her terminal cancer. Always
having known that his purpose was to write, Wilber describes how the
impact of diagnosis was for Treya an opportunity to question her life's
work. She walked a sacred path, where there was no place for bitterness.
Her energies were harnessed to find purpose. Treya viewed cancer as an
invitation to change what needed to change all along, and the couple
shared a story of rebirth: from doing to being, from controlling to
releasing, and from masculine to feminine (qualities). Wilber suggested
that an observer could have viewed his wife's experience as denial, but
in truth what he witnessed was deep transformation, as Treya stated, 'If
this is the way my life is, then this is the way my life is, and I'll live it
well,' (p. 227).

In describing his role in supporting his wife, Wilber recognises how he came to serve, but equally acknowledges how his partner also served, in walking alongside him in the cancer work they were called to do. On returning from hospital following his diagnosis, Fran said, 'Well, if we are going to have to do this, we are going to do it mindfully.' His illness was short but from the outset, I took my place alongside him and shared that intention. In recognition of remembering purpose my challenge was to trust, cultivate and hold compassion, to bear witness and stay awake to what was unfolding. And so it was that I found myself walking alongside Fran as he lived his dying. As our lives were turned into chaos, I began to let go of expectations and logical plans and attempted to live in the moment, as was his wish. Gently awakening to a new reality, I had the bizarre yet profound realisation that I had done it before and if I trusted my body and intuition all would be well. Amidst it all the profound sense of 'remembering purpose' resonated. Everything I had ever done, felt or experienced was in order to live the days from Fran's diagnosis to his last breath.

Cancer is a bloody nuisance. It interrupts lives, turns what we think we know on its head and tears to shreds the hopes and dreams that human beings have built, the imaginings of what life was going to be. Moreover, 'cancer is an existential trigger' (Tacón, 2011, p. 644) and challenges fundamentally who we are and why we are here. In the last week of his life, Fran said, 'I am my work.' Throughout his illness his intention was to bear witness to his philosophy for living. During his career Fran had over 300 publications and he was known for his creative, challenging and critical thinking, as well as his radical teaching methods. His work spanned a wide range of topics, most of them embedded in and stemming from a unitary world view, the passion of his academic life and nursing practice. He was not popular when he questioned traditional models of nurse education, arguing that we are unitary human beings, existing in a connected universe and therefore a person cannot be separated from their condition, or a patient from a nurse. In this unitary paradigm, wholeness is not an ideal but a given and we experience existence as an unbroken whole (Cowling, 2012) in which birth, death, joy and grief are not a problem requiring a label but a flow and a rhythm to be lived.

Two years before his diagnosis, Fran was awarded a scholarship and travelled to Japan, exploring and experimenting with the concept of mindfulness. Currently quite a trendy idea, mindfulness means something different to everyone who might care to give it any thought at all and there is increasing evidence to suggest that mindfulness techniques may indeed reduce stress and improve wellbeing (for example, Tacón, 2011; Liu et al., 2013). However, a paper he published following his visit to Japan offers a clue to what Fran meant by mindfulness from his personal perspective:

> I began to understand that overcoming concepts of self, being, life and soul must be accompanied by a strong social sense and consciousness. And I began to understand that this can be achieved by asking questions such as, When seeing, how do we see? When touching, how do we touch and when thinking, how do we think? (Biley, 2010, p. 2)

Whilst being still at the edge of a koi pond, Fran reflects on the words of the ancient philosopher Lao Tzu: 'Do you have the patience to wait till your mud settles and the water is clear? Can you remain unmoving until the right action arises by itself' (p. 2). Back from Japan, the phrases of Lao Tzu became familiar in our household, as (to my frustration) he would say things like, 'let the mud settle,' or 'All is well.' My cue to inwardly seethe, 'Yeh right, it's all very well sitting there being mindful but what about the bins, the school run, football practice, the washing up.'

But then our world was turned on its head. The cancer was so advanced that there was no hope of recovery, and the bins and the washing up faded into oblivion. Always a deeply sensitive and thoughtful man, in his quiet yet determined way, Fran took control sharing with me his intention to die consciously and mindfully. For him that meant living and experiencing each moment fully and in the now, letting time unfold as it was destined to do, experiencing the change, seeing and feeling in a new way. As the mud stirred, once again the words came to mind: when seeing how do we see, when touching how do we touch and when thinking how do we think? It was 4:40pm on 3rd August 2012 that we received the diagnosis of extensive cancer and widespread metastases. My journal reads:

I can only remember the doctor's first name – Stephen.
'So, curtains' you say. He said he was sorry and even
though your eyes were full of tears, you reassure him that
it was ok. 'I'm ok' you said. Turning to me you held my
hand - 'are you alright?' I nod, reverting to my default
position of being mute. I have no voice. I listen, I hear
but it is through a membrane, a bubble that somehow
engulfed us while no one was watching. Us on the inside,
the world outside. But we are safe. We are bombarded
with information.
A nurse will ring. There will be a doctor's appointment but
it is 5 o'clock on a Friday and they want to go home.

In a personal reflection, *A grief observed*, C. S. Lewis stated that
grief, 'feels like being mildly drunk, or concussed. There is a sort of
invisible blanket between the world and me' (Lewis, 1961, p. 5). So
it was true. The fear just needed a context, the demon a name. As I
drove home that day, shaking and mute, I knew that in spite of the
shock, it wasn't a surprise. For a year prior, a silent rising fear inside
of me and an intense instinct signalled that something had started to
come undone and that life was changing at the deepest level. In the
same way I knew when I was pregnant, in the same way my intuition
always told me when there was something wrong with the kids, I just
knew. On the first night of this new reality, unable to sleep, I scribbled
in my journal:

Thoughts on bubbles: foetal, fatal pain, we are trapped
inside a bubble, surrounded by people, noise and light,
and yet they cannot reach us. Like twins entwined in the
womb, we are inseparable, safe and protected.

Soon after the days were full of visits from health care professionals,
as they invaded our most sacred of spaces, our bedroom, even our bed.
It was deeply disturbing and was something I came to reflect on later,
in my loneliness and grief. My role as protector and gatekeeper to
well-meaning visitors echoed the wisest of observations that,

> There is scarcely a greater worry which invalids have
> to endure than the incurable hope of their friends ...
> who should leave off the practice of attempting to
> cheer the sick by making light of their danger and by
> exaggerating their probability of recovery.
> (Nightingale, 1859/2010, p. 68)

We were inundated with advice, that we must pray and have hope, that Fran must change his diet, eat certain foods, take supplements, have reflexology, reiki, massage, and so it went on and on. Whilst all kind, well-meaning and appreciated, it nevertheless left me feeling that somehow, I was not doing enough. Fran told me not to be ridiculous and carried on smoking regardless, wearily intimating, 'How can I make small talk when all I can think about is cancer' (Conway, 1997; cited in Carlick & Biley, 2004, p. 311). When his 'named' doctor paid her first visit, the assessment took place in Fran's shed. I smiled to myself. Fran the teacher, weaving his magic, explaining to the doctor that the mindful practice found in woodturning, be applied to living: 'When I was turning bowls, time seemed to stand still. My mind felt as though it had become empty, my thoughts and my own internal commentary seemed to disappear' (Biley, 2010, p. 2). At the funeral a few weeks later, I talked of Fran's shed, and the sacred space he created for himself there. By inviting the doctor to talk with him in his shed, Fran was allowing himself to be vulnerable, almost saying this is me, this is who I am. I often wonder if she really understood the gift he was sharing and indeed, if she has ever thought about it since.

Being authentically present and listening to another's story is described in the caritas processes as fundamental to a caring relationship. This was reinforced in those early days, as I was given the most helpful advice from my brother who also happened to be a nurse. He told me to be the listener. From diagnosis, Fran made it clear to everyone that he would be in control of how much information he needed. He stopped doctors when they went too deeply into medical jargon, insisting that he needed only enough information to live in the moment. After all, none of them really knew what would happen, when or how. Accepting this truth, at the same time I listened, reading the silence, the punctuation between the lines, body language and expression, authentically present as the surreal story took its inevitable course.

Although only a few brief weeks, the moments we shared were the most precious times, when we really began to talk and share a meaningful exploration of mindfulness and unitary consciousness. Behind the bolted bathroom door we snatched moments of silence and peace, where words were not needed. Only touch, mindful touch, as I washed Fran's thinning, emaciated body. Living in his body and accepting the changes that were occurring, it was as if he was communicating with the cancer, and with tenderness, knowing it. Reaching inside, to communicate with each cell, not driven by anger, but by wonder, acceptance, even by curiosity. Always a man of few words, Fran was still and thoughtful. Could it be that cancer as particles of energy can be reached and calmed? Like pigments of paint on an artist's brush, do they come together to complete a picture? Fran found no comfort in music or writing. After all, when faced with one's own mortality, what songs are there to listen to, what poetry is there to read, what stories to write? And so he turned to painting. Always a lover of art and inspired by Watson's Theory of Human Caring (Watson, 1988), as a newly appointed university lecturer Fran took the then, radical step of taking nursing students to art galleries to explore nursing concepts such as caring and suffering (Biley, 1992).

Our dining room was transformed into an artist's studio and roles were reversed, as ex-nursing student and friend, the effervescent Cecilia became the teacher. I remember her sitting and painting alongside Fran, as he lost himself and focused fully on the emerging picture on the canvas. Recalling his visit to Japan, Fran writes: 'The arts are not intended for utilitarian purposes only or for purely aesthetic enjoyment but are meant to train the mind, indeed bring it into contact with ultimate reality,' (Suzuki, 1999, p. 7; cited in Biley, 2010). When he could not sleep, late into the night, I would find him alone, painting. Fran would be the first to admit that he produced no great works of art but the emotion conveying the palpable agony of separation does justice to his effort. Where he could not find words, the paintings spoke and in the stirring, churning of my heart I hear and resonate with the words: 'In this contact one didn't need emotion. The intimacy was complete. Can that intimacy be love itself?' (Lewis, 1961, p. 62).

And so Fran turned to reaching inside,
his paintings spoke, poetry.
Thinning churning human pigments came together,
my heart in intimacy.
Theory on the canvas.
A picture emerging – nursing, mindful touch, cancer.
Aesthetic indeed
communicating the changes,
touch, tenderness, peace,
mortality, unitary consciousness.
Nursing transformed into living purpose.

Chapter 5

'When I don't know who I am, I serve you. When I know who I am, I am you.'
My old friend and I smiled at each other. Is this not the deepest expression of
compassion? (Halifax, 2018, p. 220)

In spite of every effort to live mindfully during those months, we
did not always manage it. Living caritas reminded me that allowing
for the expression of positive and negative feeling was part of being in
authentic caring presence but we weren't saints and there were times
when Fran was hard to like. I am sure the feeling was mutual. In spite
of our world being turned upside down, strangely life also went on and
my diary from that time records how, somehow the kids still went to
school, there were parents' evenings, haircuts, sports and music lessons,
light bulbs were changed, the roof leaked and the car broke down.
Only at night, as we lay together in our bed, could we snatch the time
to think the unthinkable … Show me how to live without you. When
sleep was elusive, I watched Fran, trying to hold on to the moment,
studying his face, hair and hands, bottling the smell of him. I have
wondered since if he did the same. Did he watch me and what was
he thinking? Sometimes I would wake to find him pacing the floor,
rubbing his lower back as he was gripped with spasms of pain. He
would snap at me to go back to sleep. I wanted to reach out and say,
'Please don't go.' Torn between everyone else's needs and the complex
and multiple responsibilities I had to carry, it is saddening now to
think that there were times when I let him down and other times
I ponder how I survived, when the self seemed to all but disappear.
Simultaneously, I contemplate stillness and if (and how) the seeds of
remembering purpose were nurtured in those grim weeks. Writing to
his young friend of sadness, Rilke (1934/1993) stated:

The moments when something new has entered into
us, something unknown; our feelings grow mute in shy
perplexity, everything withdraws and stillness comes, and
the new, which no one knows, stands in the midst of it and
is silent ... in the middle of transition, the new thing in us,
the added thing, has entered into our heart, has gone into
its inmost chamber and is not even there anymore ... is
already in our blood ... the future enters into us this way in
order to transform itself in us long before it happens
(p. 64).

Friends and a loving sister stepped in, taking care of the children,
but in spite of the kind invitations they rarely strayed far from home.
Keeping vigil. The pain was unbearable, etched on faces, seeping
into sleep patterns and eating habits. Those were dark days as we
all adjusted to change and lived with uncertainty. Whilst trying
to let the mud settle and allow the right actions to emerge, we
were also lost and fearful and our hearts were broken. But we were
blessed. So many friends, wonderful in their honesty, support and
kindness, others not quite as much, the lens of caritas helping me
to understand over time, that maybe they could only deal with their
own pain. Expressing surprise and gratitude, Fran was deeply moved
by every act of kindness and by how much he was loved. As if in
a complex dance of grief, unexpected people emerged in our lives
and some of the closest moved away. Echoing an undated journal
entry, everything, absolutely everything we think, say or do makes a
difference ... this is truth, this is karma.

And so it was that the day of the first of three chemotherapy
treatments arrived. For Fran, living in the moment did not mean
that he was passive or inert. Indeed, the opposite was true. It was his
cancer, his dying and he was determined to do it his way. There is no
record in my journal for that day, maybe because it was (and remains)
so vivid and I am comforted in the assertion that memories of illness
are 'often remarkable in their precision' (Frank, 2013, p. 59). The
nurses were kind as if they could read our fear and although it was
unusual, they found us a quiet space off the main ward so that I could
stay. After all, not being together was simply out of the question.
Time after time I was by Fran's side as thick pink and yellow bags

of fluid slowly seeped in to his veins. Speaking of marriage in the seminal poetry, *The prophet*, Gibran (1926/1991, p. 18) wrote, 'Let there be spaces in your togetherness and let the winds of heaven dance between you.' We sat. I didn't know Fran's thoughts and can't remember what we talked about during those long hours but the sacredness of the moment and our togetherness throughout, those feelings are etched on my soul.

The autumn afternoons were warm and yet as we left the hospital, Fran was wrapped in a winter scarf, hat and gloves to protect him from the natural elements that might disturb the balance of treatment, as the poison slowly absorbed into his body. Huge egg-like tablets added to the pharmacy that had taken hold in our bathroom. I was charged with the medicine round, as Fran sat in bed, harsh and hawk-like in his observation of such a junior nurse. One of the lesser known side effects of his chemotherapy was extreme sensitivity to cold or metal objects. On one occasion, a friend was in the kitchen when Fran came in to make himself a sandwich. Because he could not touch anything cold, I asked if I could help and I got something out of the freezer. It was an everyday occurrence, us moving around the kitchen, walking alongside, doing our stuff, but my friend commented that in that act she had never seen so much love. In the same way I had witnessed with Liam so many years before, she knew something special was going on. Did she witness a caring moment? So often love is manifest in the most mundane of actions, like getting something out of the freezer because someone can't do it, or like our last ever Facebook messaging conversation on 30th September, that reads:

> Me: Have you decided – leek or mushroom?
> Fran: Mushroom please with buttered toast soldiers ...

It was a moment of silliness really. I was in the kitchen, Fran was in bed and we were just mucking about, I mean toast soldiers? Most days when we weren't together we would send each other numerous texts, emails or Facebook messages but who would have thought that such an ordinary discussion about the choice of soup would be our last written exchange? In the early days after his death, I salvaged some of his emails and text messages. Most of them are mundane, about everyday things such as – at the petrol station - do we need milk, that sort of thing, but in reading them I hear and remember so vividly the candid tone of his voice, the dry, cynical humour and overall monosyllabic grumpiness or gentle kindness depending on mood.

The pattern of chemotherapy did not suit, his body and soul were just too tired. Fran was open to the possibility that this virulent route may be an option in order to have more time, but accepted how it unfolded. Prone to being autocratic under pressure, it was at this point that Fran made the unilateral decision that I was to sleep in the study adjacent to our bedroom. Feeling banished and rejected I spent several sleepless nights in tears, mourning my unravelling marriage crashing to a premature end. Five days after the first treatment, he cried out in the middle of the night as the cruel side effects of the treatment took their grip. Restoring the balance, I vowed that come what may, I would not be leaving our bed again, and I kept that promise. Within 6 days, the first cycle of chemotherapy was stopped. This was the pattern of the next two treatments. Each time, Fran was convinced that the cancer was shrinking and that he was putting on weight. I smiled and lovingly accepted his truth, but what I saw was not weight gain but a distended abdomen and a wasting body. There were subtle changes to his skin, as what were once the distinguished lines across the forehead became fine wrinkles on tissue. My heart was breaking as I authentically listened to his story, bearing witness to the change and trying hard to live only in the moment, as was his wish.

Events unfolded further when Fran, experiencing the excruciating side effects of the second cycle of chemotherapy, collapsed on the bathroom floor. Unable to get him up, I gathered blankets and pillows to make him comfortable, improvising in the moment to create warmth and security. I am here. After 2 hours a doctor came and as he rummaged through the plethora of medicine on the shelf, my intuition told me that he was uncomfortable and did not know what to do. As he crouched on the floor next to Fran, I put my hand on the doctor's knee, looked him in the eye and reassured him that we were letting the process unfold and we would take responsibility. No heroics. No hospitalisation. No resuscitation. In the meantime the children came home to face the absolute shock of their dad being so ill. But angels were there in my beautiful sister and lovely friend. They scooped them up, as I was forced to rush back to the bathroom to maintain the vigil on the floor by Fran's side, witnessing the moment, watching, waiting, ready to serve.

In her observations of being alongside the dying, Monika
Renz (2015) identified how an individual's perception of self and
personhood alters as they move towards transition and as the
inevitability of death moves towards them. At this threshold, it is
not unusual for instinctive, primordial fear to manifest. As a nurse
I have cared for many people at the end of life and witnessed the
shame of vulnerability, the shift in the dynamics of relationships,
fear of the unknown, of letting go and of not being loved. Dying
is an unravelling of who you are, stripping away identity, roles and
responsibilities, ultimately challenging fundamentally what we think
we know (Kübler-Ross & Kessler, 2000). Excruciatingly, Levine
(1986) asks:

> Who is the person who doesn't have the strength to chew?
> Who has to concentrate just to swallow?
> Where is the person who had all those social
> and sexual, intellectual and physical identities?
> You're watching your body get weaker and weaker.
> You can't take care of the children. You can't make love.
> You can't earn your living. You can't even go to the
> bathroom by yourself. Who are you now? (p. 56)

Although the notion of vigil may be synonymous with religious
ritual, in the context of being alongside the dying this is not so.
Being fully present in the moment, offering comfort, gentleness and
compassion, holding intention, creating safe space, touching, gently
administering personal care or simply, 'just being there'. These are the
most devotional acts of love. This is vigil. Offering a more direct and
simplified approach, Halifax (2008) argues that the most important
act of compassion is to simply 'show up,' and remember that it is 'not
what we do but how we are' (p. 105).

Sitting on the bathroom floor, it was a moment of intense human
connectedness and I was reminded that the dying are our teachers.
The sense of being open to unfolding moments was intense as
Fran groaned in confusion and discomfort. I experienced a deep
remembering that we had been here before, except it was me moaning

in childbirth and he the comforter, the protector, the companion. With this flash of realisation I knew that we had been through this and much more, perhaps in many lifetimes and that all would be well. Months later as I listened to a track by our favourite band, Everything But The Girl, tears welled up in my chest as I heard the words, 'When we face what we're afraid of, we find out what we're made of' (1994). I certainly found out what I was made of that day.

Like fine wrinkles,
pattern became his truth,
In vigil,
intuition reassured my heart,
unfolding moments held witness
mindfulness, the turning tide.

Chapter 6

I stand in front of you. I'll take the force of the blow. Protection.
You're a boy and I'm a girl but you know you can lean on me.
And I don't have no fear. I'll take on any man here who
says that's not the way it should be. (Thorn, 2015)

Like flotsam on the sea, we were sometimes held in calm and sometimes battered by raging storms but there was always the constant of the turning tide. Having no recollection of events and wondering what all the fuss was about, Fran was back with us, feeling well, putting affairs in order, full of hopes and dreams of holidays and returning to work. There were even 2 occasions when Fran felt well enough to drive out to the coast and we enjoyed expensive, intimate lunches as if on a first date. I shared his optimism whilst comforting our distraught and confused children who were puzzled by their dying father's new found energy. Living the paradox of hope and denial was a personal struggle and yet the intention to live in the moment and uphold authentic caring presence remained paramount. Fran said that we were 'negotiating uncertainty,' and on reflection it is clear that he drew on the experience of his own, then current academic work, the development of a Negotiating Uncertainty Tool. Grounded theory research with men adapting to a diagnosis of HIV positive, suggested that uncertainty emerged when time and health were threatened. Uncertainty cannot be eliminated, only negotiated. Setting goals and making lifestyle changes may help reduce uncertainty (Perrett & Biley, 2013a, 2013b). Always a passionate nurse and teacher at heart, Fran had the intention of telling his story of negotiating uncertainty and was meeting his close friend and colleague Stephanie Perrett to begin the work. Sadly, the day she came to the house was the day he died.

A dedicated supervisor and friend, Fran believed his teaching and nursing practice were one and that his role was merely to be with others in a mutual process of learning. In his kind and gentle approach to teaching I was always reminded of words in *The prophet* and at the funeral a friend read:

> 'Speak to us of Teaching.' And he said:

>> No man can reveal to you aught but that which already lies half asleep in the dawning of your knowledge. The teacher who walks in the shadow of the temple, among his followers, gives not of his wisdom but rather of his faith and lovingness. If he is indeed wise he does not bid you enter the house of his wisdom, but rather leads you to the threshold of your own mind. (Gibran, 1926/1991, p. 76)

Remembering his own nurse training days, Fran was safe being cared for by students and junior nurses, putting them at ease, even in the most complicated and uncomfortable procedures, remaining in control through his own stillness and meditation. On the day of diagnosis my journal reads:

> I brought your clothes in and you got dressed, but we were told that we needed to see the doctor before you were discharged. We sat and talked about the student nurse that had been looking after you. She was lovely and you told her that she would make a good nurse. She was embarrassed, looking after her lecturer but was smart and confident enough to ask to sit in when we went in for our meeting with the doctor. She gave me tissues. As we walked away from the hospital we said goodbye. Her teacher as well as her patient, you saw her through that day as if it was some clinical exercise. I wonder if, like my experience with Liam 30 years before, that day will stay with her for ever. Will it define her career? … So much for a young nurse to carry.
> Did she go home and cry?

Fran always made time for his students and over the years our house was continually open to nurses who were travelling or studying a long way from home, especially at Christmas or holiday time. Not surprising then that on one of his few good days, he chose to go out for a drive with one of his students. I expressed concern but Fran explained to me that he was going because it was important to the student. Although they had planned a day out, they returned home after a couple of hours. Fran was exhausted and spent the rest of the day in bed, but he remained glad that they had spent the time together. At the funeral, our friend Stephanie read her own personal tribute:

> Fran was quite simply the most extraordinary teacher. He lived out the philosophy by which he taught, he taught not through papers or PowerPoint or lectures. Fran taught by the way he lived, he taught through constant exploration and enquiry, a passionate desire to know and understand the relationships of the world whilst knowing that knowledge only brings further questions. Fran taught through friendship, through interactions with others and the natural world around him. He did not ask his students to agree, he desired not to be followed. He asked simply for a willingness to explore new things, to embrace the experience of learning in whatever form it may take, to open the mind and cherish the surprises that may lie ahead. I visited Fran, not knowing it would be the last day of his earthly life, our words were brief and yet with the little energy he had he asked me to make sure I picked up a textbook from the study, for some work we had planned to take forward. He taught until the very end.

As time went on, our already quirky, dishevelled home fell into more and more disarray, as there were just not enough hours in the day. Almost without exception health care professionals were kind, caring, sensitive and considerate, but were nevertheless, a reminder of the storm upon us. My role as protector echoed Rilke's assertion that the 'highest task between two people is to protect the solitude of the other' (Rilke, 1934/1993, p. 54) and as a man who cherished stillness, Fran charged me with shielding him from well-meaning but unwelcome visitors, who were 'never more than a painful annoyance' (Nightingale 1859/2010, p. 38), in the plethora of assessments and interviews they were required to undertake. In spite of their values and intentions, specialists dominated and patronised with their expertise. The inequality of Fran as patient and them as expert irritated us both. They didn't see us. Even though our home had become a route for health care traffic of all types, essentially we felt alone and violated, struggling to establish any helping, trusting, caring relationships outside ourselves. One of the most painful days was when a solicitor called and Fran signed his will. He snapped and was cruel and spent the rest of the day with his back to me. Understandable of course but it hurt nevertheless and I was tearful. Having witnessed my love literally sign his life away, it was not one of our best days, as intention and mindfulness slipped into an abyss of raw humanity. My journal from that time reminds me, how I prayed 'for enough light to see a divine sense in the world, enough faith to follow the light and love to make the darkness tolerable' (West, 1981 p. 223). In the seminal work, *Being with Dying*, the Buddhist teacher Joan Halifax reminds us that being alongside others at the end of life requires courage. Acknowledging pain, fear and unfinished business often means accepting the unacceptable and continuing to 'show up' is what love asks of us (Halifax 2008, p. 105). Having accepted that our intention was to live mindfully, my act of caritas was to practise loving kindness and to hold the intention in the moments when he was not able to do it for himself, when he was too tired or sick or sad, when mindfulness slipped into the painful reality of chemotherapy, diarrhoea, vomiting and pain.

Whilst Fran's world dissolved as he transitioned into death, the space we had created over the years became at the same time a reminder of ephemerality and a place of familiarity, safe and gentle continuity. Initially, when pondering Caring Science and in particular the caritas process of 'creating a healing environment for authentic caring presence' (Watson, 2008), I felt some guilt at the disorder and turmoil that our bedroom, our sacred space had become. By nature Fran was not the tidiest of people, in fact he was a messy bugger and his apparent disregard for my need for tidiness and order was always a source of tension. He was at his most comfortable when surrounded by the same clutter of books, old furniture, Indian miniature ornaments, art and personal belongings and this did not change. Not for him the flowers, candles, essential oils and paraphernalia associated with creating a healing environment, rather, the authentic, eccentric chaos, so quintessentially Fran. He was one of the first nurses in the UK to embrace and understand what became known as energy field pattern manifestation (Rogers, 1970), the idea that the physical environment is not the be all and end all, rather it is what we are, 'we are already the space for the world, we are consciousness itself' (Tolle, 2009, cited in Jonas-Simpson, 2010, p. 197), in other words, we are the environment, the rest for him was just stuff and trimmings, unimportant to who he was.

In contrast, my attention to the physical environment that was our home took on a different tone. Driven by intuitive, almost primal instinct, in the hours Fran slept, I found myself spring cleaning, rearranging cupboards and sorting out old clothes. When sweeping the backyard, I was struck by a deep remembering and realised that in the same way I prepared for childbirth, I was preparing for death to come to us. In anticipation of the unknown, I was nesting, overwhelmed with the urgent need to create a safe and secure space for my babies, my beloved. As a woman's body returns to its most visceral state, doing what it has to do, the baby too, knowing it is time, braces to come into the world. And I ponder, in the same way we know how to be born and to give birth, do we also know how to die? A woman's instinct to nest in quiet, undisturbed space is a trait also found at the end of life. But this is a fragile balance, so easily disturbed and fractured by noise, light, unexpected complications and unwelcome interventions, in turn leading to deep distress and trauma (Renz, 2015). From experience I knew that in contrast to the busy hospital settings where I gave birth, my task was to be the authentic presence, to create and sustain the loving environment in which Fran chose to die. It was a bizarre yet profound realisation, and I was reassured again that I had done this before and if I trusted my body and my intuition, all would be well.

Since that time, staying awake to intuition, quietly and steadily watching, waiting and trusting what I know has continued to be a strength and asset. The effect of the experience led me to search out evidence of other women's stories. Although conducted many years ago, the research study, *Women's ways of knowing* (Belenky et al., 1997), offered groundbreaking insights in how women produce, understand, experience and value knowledge, highlighting how women learn through life experience, in relationships, families and communities (Goldberger, 1996a). Although in retrospect there were limitations to the study, for example a lack of diversity and the focus on western epistemologies, nevertheless it was a springboard for new approaches to research, learning and patterns of knowing. In seeking to understand situations, the women in the study demonstrated multiple patterns of knowing and illustrated how both having a voice and respect for the inner voice were a key to knowledge (Belenky et al., 1997). Innate qualities such as empathy, intuition, instinct and care were recognised and valued as wisdom. As one woman stated:

> There's a part of me that I didn't even know I had until recently – instinct, intuition, whatever. It helps me and protects me. It's perceptive and astute. I just listen to the inside of me and I know what to do. (p. 52)

The innate qualities and multiple ways of knowing described by Belenky et al. (1997) may well be ancient wisdom and knowledge that has been lost in the mist of time, begging the question how, when and why such wisdom was crushed. Feminist scholars have argued that in a culture where reason is set against emotion, and masculine against feminine, it is not surprising that women may 'doubt the authority of their own experience' (Debold, Tolman & Mikel Brown, 1996, p. 107). And yet:

> The body knows. It's amazing that we can carry on so many different processes, electrochemical, hormonal – that is all a knowingness ... there is a much greater intelligence than I will ever be able to be conscious of... When I know something it is just this inward sense of like listening with all of me and when it comes out it does not come out in parts, it is like a big picture. This is what I think intuition is – the brain's more efficient way of being able to process all this amazing information from everywhere, from the whole universe, and bring it into this kind of full blown moment, of like ah-ha (Goldberger, 1996b, p. 355).

Uncertainty reared its ugly head again when blood results showed a poor prognosis. As the concept of time began to shift we thought and lived in terms of days, hours and moments. With birthdays approaching, Fran took the lead in ordering and wrapping presents and he decided to try a third and final cycle of chemotherapy, with the faint thought of making it through, maybe even to Christmas, which although only weeks away was as surreal as travelling to the moon. We managed to go out for a family birthday meal and the photographs we took that night were the last ones of us together. He looked so ill and his eyes mirrored the pain in his soul. With a broken heart I tried and continue to try, every moment, to sustain love and hope and hold what is left of our little family together.

The soul nesting.
Mystery weaves, memory twinges
Rearranging time and mind,
re-patterning birth.

Chapter 7

For what is it to die but to stand naked in the wind and melt into the sun.
And when the earth shall claim your limbs, then you shall truly dance
(Gibran, 1926/1991, p. 109).

Living mindfully, in the moment is one thing, being prepared quite another. During those weeks I lived the paradox of trusting and being in the moment, whilst knowing that it was only a matter of time before I was alone. Fran's wish was to die at home. However, like a mother planning a home birth, we were persuaded that a backup plan may be helpful and so I visited the hospice. It was a bright place, with a strangely cheery atmosphere that unsettled me. Although on reflection I realised my first impressions were unfair, at the time I could not see beyond the superficiality of the setting and came away feeling more isolated than ever, knowing that it was down to me to be the authentic presence. My learning from the experience was to be more mindful and in the moment. After all, events would unfold as they were destined to do. When would death come to us? How would it unfold? What about the children? Like waiting for the first twinges of labour, we waited and took the leap of faith that all would be well, open to the spiritual and to mystery.

Once again, diarrhoea and vomiting took their grip upon Fran's emaciated body. Time was meaningless. As the days and nights started to merge I lay next to him, ready to jump whenever I heard him retch, holding and emptying the vomit bowl, time and time and time again. I showed up. I watched and waited, keeping vigil and doing my best to hold dignity and compassion. I studied every line of his face and hands, the changing shape of his body, the sinking cheek bones and thinning hair on the pillow. Entering a dimension where I could not reach him, Fran shook me to tell me that he was going out for dinner with friends in Greenwich Village. I smiled, 'Have a nice time,' and he drifted off to sleep.

Mindfulness practice is 'so easy to say, so difficult to do' (Biley, 2010, p. 4), especially when tested to the brink of our humanity. As

Fran weakened, the doctors were increasingly concerned and wanted
to admit him to the hospital. He refused and snapped, telling me that
he 'Didn't want me hanging around, looking at him, doing nothing. I
am alone! You think you are there for me but you can't be. Go away.' A
few minutes later he called, 'Where have you been? I want you here.'
It was harsh and cruel but it was the closest he came to anger. I held
the intention and his comments, like so many before, were absorbed.
I prayed for light, understanding that I could go so far with him and
no further and knowing that I was not and never could be enough. At
that point, Fran could have given into fear and hopelessness, given over
decision-making and care to others, and succumbed to the oblivion
of sedation, but his wish was to die consciously. As every aspect of
past, future, the closest roles and relationships, and the body physical
melted away, the decision to live his dying was matched with immense
courage in facing his inevitable aloneness.

At daybreak, once again, crouching by our bed, the doctor tried
to persuade Fran to go in to hospital and again he refused. The
discussion was awkward and nasty. The doctor on the one hand,
desperate to grasp at any intervention that would delay the inevitable,
and Fran, on the other, asserting his right to live his dying, refusing to
be robbed of the precious space where he was safe and loved. Looking
me in the eye, Fran said, 'You have to back me up on this one.' And I
did. Wholeheartedly. Behind closed doors, I cried in my sister's arms,
then wiped away my tears and got on with it. Sitting by our bedside I
found comfort in emailing Fran's nursing family in America who love
him so much. That evening one beautiful friend wrote:

> It sounds like Fran's condition is definitely on the down
> slope and that he is in a transition toward the other side. It
> is so great that you are a nurse and can take care of him in
> your home. I am crying as I write this email and my heart
> goes out to you. Yes, please keep me posted. I will let the
> community know that Fran is in transition now.

To know that we were held in love during those days was not only
an immense comfort, but gave a deep sense of peace and intense
connection. Although so far away from family and isolated in so
many ways, we were not alone in holding the vigil. I knew that Fran

was close to leaving me. So weak from vomiting and diarrhoea he said, 'I have had enough.' I rubbed his arm and said, 'I know.'

What came to be Fran's last was a harrowing day of collapse, exhaustion, doctors and paramedics. Helping him to the bathroom, once again he slid to the floor, so weak he could just not get it together. In spite of assurances that assistance would come, on calling for paramedic help to get him back to bed, I was curtly informed that it was not an emergency and we would have to wait at least 3 hours. Shocked and appalled by this abrupt and rude treatment at such a critical time, the overwhelming feeling was of isolation and of the outside world having no rights here in the most sacred of space. I deeply believe that the National Health Service is full of amazing human beings but as is so often the case, in spite of good intention, procedure and bureaucracy create rules that can distance and dehumanise, sadly at the most desperate of times. However, in spite of this, when the paramedics did arrive, they could not have been more reassuring or kind. Bless them. Once again the scenario unfolded on the bathroom floor and once again we were open to mystery. Fran was resolute in experiencing his dying and wishing to stay alert, he resisted suggestions of sedative medication. Even though there was no blood pressure, pulse or blood sugar reading, Fran remained in control of the situation and to everyone's astonishment asked for a cup of tea. However, amidst all of the busyness there was a peace and a stillness that was serene, and a profound and strong but silent sense of dignity in ministering loving care to meet the most basic of human needs. A year later, reading the *Tibetan book of living and dying* (Rinpoche, 1992), I am humbled but not surprised to see that Fran's determination to remain lucid is not unusual in those who choose the path of mindful, conscious dying.

With the assistance of the paramedics I helped Fran back to bed and they left. He felt hot and restless and yet his body was cold. It was my fourth day without sleep, so as he settled I lay next to him and dozed, for perhaps an hour. All of a sudden he sat upright and swung his legs out of bed. Jumping up, I ran to him, afraid that he might fall. 'Oh you're there' were the last words he spoke as he fell forward into my arms. It was 4:30pm. By 4:39pm Fran had passed. Those 9 minutes were and will remain the most profound of my life and I observed how, just as a soul is in transition in birth, so it is in death. Rinpoche (1992) suggests that it may be hard to maintain awareness and light, even for the most conscious being and that the moment of death may be chaotic if not held through mindfulness and meditation. As Fran's physical power drained away there was pure love and connection. I told him that it was okay to go. Go to the light. Don't be frightened. Body limp and eyes staring blankly, into a space beyond the autumn leaves falling from the trees in front of our bedroom window. Go, go to the light. Fran's constant companion, his beloved cat Ariel, purred as she slept on, curled in the space where his feet had been seconds before. Like the anticipation of a baby's first breath, I waited, the panting slowly getting shallower and gentler, as Fran's final breath faded and then stopped, holding the space, the silence, the light, I don't know how long for. And then. And then for the last time I tended to Fran's body, with honour and with dignity: "When seeing, how do we see? When touching, how do we touch and when thinking, how do we think?" (Biley, 2010, p. 2).

I had not considered what might unfold in the period between death and Fran leaving the house but there was an intense feeling that we were at a precipice, the edge of mystery. In the renowned text on dying, *The four things that matter most*, Byock (2014) suggested that in letting go of the tangle of fear, anger and confusion, the true nature of the human spirit, love, patience, forgiveness and compassion, may come to the fore. But for me in that moment, in that place, there was no anger, fear or confusion, rather a sense of chronological time dissolving, as knowing and intuition led to the creation of our own ritual in that sacred space. Again I was stirred at the deepest level. I knew what to do. I had done it before. Fran's last Christmas present to me, a book of poetry, *The seasons of the soul* by Hermann Hesse, lay on the table next to the bed. I picked it up and read:

This day had made me tired.
I wish to sleep
and welcome the starlight
like a child after play.
Hands of mine, stop doing.
Mind of mine, stop thinking.
All my senses are getting ready
to sink soon into slumber and sweet sleep.
No longer fettered, my soul slips free,
ready to soar upwards in its infinite flight,
to live fully its thousand lives
in the magic journeys of the night.
(Hesse, 2011, p. 76)

Later that night I emailed a friend:

Fran passed over to the light this afternoon. He died
peacefully in my arms. We were in a circle of light and love.
He was at home, in his own bed, which was what he wished
for. He was so loved and so brave. We then lit candles and
incense and played his favourite piece of music, which was
Vaughan Williams, 'Lark ascending'. I told him that it was
okay to go to the light.
Bless him.

And a text from a friend read:

Fran, so glad you passed as you would have wished,
peacefully, with your lovely family by your side. A candle
burns in our house lighting the way for you on your journey ...

Like a pane of glass between heaven and earth cracking, shattering
and raining down on us, the pain was excruciating. However, it
had never occurred to me that I wouldn't organise the funeral and
spontaneously Fran's beloved students gathered, surrounded and
supported me in planning and delivering his last master class. The
setting was woodland, on a remote wild and windswept hill, with
breathtaking views of the English countryside all around us. What

unfolded was the wholehearted co-creation of a unique, Fran-shaped-ritual and sacred space in which to celebrate, honour and remember. Connected and held in the love of others across the world, it was a reminder of how one person can make a difference, how the smallest actions ripple and change the lives of others and how we exist in a unitary universe. His passion and contribution to nursing particularly shone through as scores of letters, emails and Facebook tributes were shared. What was, on the surface a little gathering of a hundred people on an English hillside, became a global event:

> I am someone whose life changed by knowing
> Fran and changed irreversibly.
> His love of the esoteric stretched minds ...
> A brilliant and compassionate soul who touched many ...
> A dedicated and dynamic scholar with
> a tremendous passion for nursing.
> He taught us to challenge, to rethink and to transform,
> lessons that have stayed with me throughout my career ...
> The passion he displayed towards everything he did and
> spoke of was inspirational. He influenced me forever ...
> My guiding force in dark days.
> I can honestly say I would not be where I
> am today without your help and guidance ...
> Thank you for your love of your fellow human beings
> made visible through your actions to make
> a positive difference in the world.
> He touched many lives and will continue to do so ...
> Fran is of the fabric that stays with you.
> His caring and love ripples infinitely, unbounded.
> Happy travelling bro – The song goes on ...
> Always remember Fran was the best of men.

My inner voice tells me that all will be well.
The dying are our teachers.
Human need, the silent sense of
dignity in ministering loving care
is remembering purpose.
Poetry like autumn leaves falling in sacred space
shapes my soul in light.

Chapter 8

And so you see I have come to doubt all that I once held as true.
I stand alone without beliefs. The only truth I know is you.
(Paul Simon, 1965/2004)

When we moved in together we slept on a mattress on the floor.
When we could afford it we bought a pine bed frame from a furniture
clearance sale and the old mattress fit perfectly. Five years later, a
severance payment bought us a brand new bed. The old one, with
its stained and stinky mattress, was demoted to the spare room and
shame on us, has lasted 25 years! The new bed was ugly, nothing
romantic or enticing but it became the bed we subsequently shared for
16 years, the place in which we loved and loathed each other, in which
we were as intimate as we were chasms apart. Snuggling and close
as soul mates or back to back as strangers, love and anger, kindness
and resentment, rising and falling, ripping each other apart and yet
embroidered together like a well-worn quilt. It was the bed that
Fran was to spend his last days in, where I lay next to him, as days
merged into night and back again, where our love and relationship
reached a depth and connection we never could have imagined. The
bed where he died also became the place where memories and grief
played themselves out as doubt and anger began to surface. I reflected
how the bed became the place where, to my fury, a doctor perched
uninvited to deliver a death sentence, where nurses and therapists in
their ill-thought-out attempts to get close to the patient in reality
distanced and isolated us. Their violation of our space divorced us
from them. Insulated and safe in those final days that room, our bed
became our world.

For over 5 hours, Fran lay in that bed. Dead. I lay with him, talking,
crying, honouring him, thanking him, knowing that the time was
getting closer, closing in on us and the body in which his soul and
spirit dwelt would be gone for ever. As I lay with him, studying for
one last time the contours of his face, the lines, inhaling him, feeling
his unshaven face, my sister crept into the room. She lay with me

and held me. I have never felt so much love as I did in that moment. I remember how we lit candles, burned incense and played music. When his body was taken I sprinkled fresh lavender buds on the bare mattress, the shape of him still visible, carved out over the years. Immersed in grief, every day for 2 weeks I knelt by the bed and rested my head on that spot, rubbing the smell of lavender into the mattress and every day replacing it with fresh buds to keep the scent alive. It may seem strange but throughout Fran's illness, and indeed since, I had a strong sense that somehow I knew what to do and I was not surprised as I later discovered how, particularly in Buddhist traditions, creating rituals and sacred space in death may help in grief and the use of herbs in these rituals is not unusual. But the bed stayed empty and the room, fading with his energy was cathedral silent.

What was odd was that when Fran was ill, I imagined that one of the first things I would do, would be to buy a new bed and exorcise the sweaty, faecal and pear sweet acid smelling memories of death. But I could not bring myself to do it. Instead the Fran-shaped hollow of the old mattress became my sacred space. Out of desperation and exhaustion, after 2 or 3 weeks I made the bed with fresh sheets. As I lay there on his side of the bed, moulded in his space, he wrapped me in his arms, his warmth and energy keeping me safe. Sometimes he came back to me in my dreams. Talking and sharing, we are happy there and in contrast to dark days, my dreams were always full of the brightest, purest light. In one dream we were in a round, pale blue room at the top of a tower. My journal recollects the encounter, written as if in a letter to him:

> A box. Old and rectangular, not quite a suitcase. A box. You open it and inside there are multi-coloured balls of light. Tonight I feel a boost like a bolt of electricity, recharging my spirit. Though my future is blank, change and a new life is possible and I can move another step.

In my dreams, Fran was always wearing something different. Sometimes he would wake me up, 'Come on, we have to do stuff.' 'What?' I asked. 'We're going camping.' 'Where?' 'Llandrindod.' 'Wales?' I asked again. 'Yes you daft bugger, come on!' In the dream I woke up and realised it was a dream. I reached out to try to hold on to it, then I woke up in our bed, alone and missing my man. Sometimes it was hard to shake off those dreams and I would go through the day feeling sad and preoccupied, unable to ground myself. Other times I drew energy and strength from my nighttime rendezvous with my dead husband. However, most of the time my mind remained and remains muddled and full of crap. On so many occasions, in the wee small hours, when sleep eluded me I would write in my journal:

> I thought I saw you today in the crowd. You were talking to a busker in the street. I saw your hat, your red frayed jumper, jeans, boots, khaki shoulder bag, your hair, your unshaven profile. I wanted to run to you. Hug you so badly!! You turned and I recoiled in pain and shock. You see for those few seconds I forgot you were dead and there, in the middle of the street the tears came. Again. Without warning, from the salty spring that is inside my chest. When stirred the tears just appear, in a deluge of pain and sadness and emptiness and loneliness. I was so lonely, walking away from that man who I so desperately wanted to be you. My head ached, my ears, my throat. I was so drained and exhausted I just went to bed and withdrew. For the first time in over a year it hit me at another level. I have nothing left to look forward to. No one will ever hold me or kiss me ever again. I will never feel someone so close that I know every fibre, smell, wrinkle and grey hair. The fold of hands, the distinct curl of toe nails, every detail of a person. And I wonder whose arms will I die in or does it no longer matter because they won't be yours. I am sad today. So very sad.

The first night when we got the news that Fran's cancer was terminal, we lay side by side and I wondered if I would ever sleep again as I listened to my heart thumping and bursting out of my chest. It felt physically heavy, as if replaced by a stone and even after 6 years, the pain is still there. It hurts. So this is how a broken heart feels.

I could not part with Fran's pillow. It was where his head lay in the last hours of his life and the first few hours of death. I cuddled that pillow every night for 3 years until the time was right to usher out the old and welcome in the new. It hurt and I cried. Familiar waves of tears and grief once again swallowed me up, my heart desperately screaming to hold on, my inner voice gently coercing me to let a little bit more of him go. So I went shopping! Alone in a huge outlet store, I made my way to the bed linen department, in search of a new quilt cover, pillow cases and sheets. Gulping in and almost choking on repressed sobs, I found myself naturally propelled towards reds, oranges and shades of gold, autumn colours that we would have chosen together. With slight trepidation I was shaken with the realisation that this was a turning point, a gift and an opportunity to consciously make a choice for me. Tentatively and with intention I started to see other spectrums of light and colour, styles, patterns and shades that Fran would never have considered. Ultimately I made the choice of pastel pink and turquoise in a paisley design. A small act in the grand scheme of things, but it was a massive, liberating step in the murky labyrinth of grief.

A year on and a lovely new bed was my birthday treat. A nod, a gentle acknowledgement that time, as ever, is passing by. My diary recalls that it was 9th June 2015:

> Two and a half years on and the bed is going today. I sit here in the space we shared so intimately for so long. Holes and broken drawers, worn springs and a sallow, discoloured, unpicked mattress could tell so many stories of birth and death, sickness and love. But it is time to let it go now. Time for new beginnings. A new space, without you. My heart is hurting and my eyes sting but I am ready to face it because it is what I must do.

And so as if another twist of my bruised heart, a wave of fear and pain, a letting go and a deep inner knowing that it was time. Before the old broken bed was taken away, I stole an hour, lit the lavender oil burner, closed the bedroom door and for one last time sat by the bed, hugging my knees, staring out of the window, reflecting on the beech trees and fields beyond, the familiar view from our bedroom that was Fran's last. In time, I watched as deliverymen dismantled the bed, carried it out of the house and tossed it in the back of a van. I then dared to let in the most agonising, unspoken memory of all. When

Fran was lifted from our bed, the funeral directors wrapped him in a white sheet, ever so tenderly, as if he were a baby. As they lifted, his arm fell loosely. I jumped as the gentle giants tenderly gathered the wayward limb and tucked it closely to his body. On a cold, pitch dark November night they took my love away. Closing the door on him for the last ever time was the loneliest moment of my life.

I wanted to run to you not ready for life alone,
happy times, swallowed and sallow
wrapped in murky bed sheets.
Death bursting out of worn springs
embroidered a familiar connection,
muddled happy talk
and dark sweet acid feeling
lay uninvited on that pillow.
The smell of romantic hot sheets roll
into encrusted lavender scent of
violated dreams rising, unspoken
twists my throat and hands
so many stories of grief and frayed shame,
memories untamed, death.
But the bed stayed empty.

I wake up five years later my bruised heart recollects
repressed lonely tears and grief.
Alone in this bed I reach out still
missing his body and gentle love.
Multi-coloured new beginnings
shade the old and curl
a labyrinth of tender dreams,
cathedral silent, pastel pink contours warm my heart.
Propelled in a strangely whipped fog
of lavender and gold my dreams
touch the place beyond anger
a window of comfort yet
restless still I pine to find him.

Chapter 9

You howled with your sound turned off and your screen dark
For tragedy to go on – to hell with the curtain.
(Hughes, 1998, p.77)

And so, as chronological time has flown by so quickly, I stand
before you Dear Reader, in the now: older, wiser, still broken, lonely
and sad and yet someone who is also so much more than that. I am
someone who is healing, finding a voice and a confidence in being
in the world. I am parenting alone, making decisions about the most
mundane and complex of issues. I wish I could write of joy and
healing, and offer you a magic solution to pain and grief and loss
but I can't. I wish I could say that living caritas, Caring Science, has
offered me resolution and healing but that would not be true.

In his observation of personal grief, C. S. Lewis wrote that, 'No
one ever told me that grief felt so much like fear. I am not afraid but
the sensation is like being afraid, the same fluttering in the stomach,
the same restlessness, the yawning,' (1961, p. 5). Looking back there
have been many dark, sad, lonely days and even more grey 'kind of
nothing' days. My journal speaks of a heavy stone that has replaced
where my heart used to be. It's painful. It hurts. So this is how a
broken heart feels. True to my pattern, I take solace in books. Reading
the literature classic *Jane Eyre* one rainy weekend, for the umpteenth
time, I saw with fresh eyes how much the author knew of grief: 'I
see a white cheek and a faded eye but no trace of tears. I suppose
then, your heart has been weeping blood,' (Brontë, 1847/1995, p.
326). Most days I still feel as though I have forgotten something or
that something is missing and then, 'comes a sudden jab of red-hot
memory,' (Lewis, 1961, p. 6). There have been joyful days where,
in stillness and silence, my inner voice has whispered, 'Stay awake!
Remember purpose. Remember what you are here to do…' But many
journal entries remind me that mostly, it has been a tumultuous ride,
a fractured and fragile path. I wish that I could draw a conclusion and
bring a happy ending to the story but I can't.

On ethical principle in writing this story, I have made minimal reference to our children. They have their own views and memories and their own story to tell. However, witnessing their pain and struggles as they face the world without their father remains the most excruciating source of heartache for me:

> Through birthdays, Christmases, anniversaries and Father's
> Days, the pain rumbles on. The hole that is Fran-shaped
> is felt acutely by all of us. And I don't have any answers.
> Sometimes I wish I knew what the question is,
> but I don't and I am bewildered.

In an attempt to show that life goes on we bravely went on holidays, but my effort to make new memories was just too painful and in retrospect seems almost pathetic. Who was I trying to kid?

> Making new memories and experiences when you are not
> here is impossible. I am sad. I live with a broken heart,
> struggling to hold on, when I am not the one they want
> or need. How do I walk alongside? Only in remembering
> who I am, can I maintain and grow in resilience and
> strength and be there.

Journalling continued to reveal a pattern of paradox, of stillness and despair. My heart crying out, be still, be still, be still and watch the deer, hear the birds, feel the stars and breathe in the crisp cold stillness of the night air, but it is as though I tempted fate as once again out of nowhere something comes to knock me off my feet. A further entry reflects the inner turmoil:

Sitting by the pond, watching the dog scurry around chasing squirrels, I am thinking about Fran, sitting by a koi pond (Biley, 2010), and the words of Lao Tzu, to have patience, let the mud settle. My life is so often just swirling mud! As soon as it starts to settle someone or something takes a big stick, hits me over the head with it and stirs it all up again! That's how I feel. So many times I have pondered how I can remember purpose when my life is so unsettled, so isolated from friends and family who I love the most. Staring into the pond, the stillness of the mirrored image reminds me that, only by having patience and letting the mud settle will remembering purpose emerge.

As my true nature struggled against the reality of life and loss, I stayed strong and stoic, breathing it in. Holding the pain in my chest and throat, I ;howled with the sound turned off,' (Hughes, 1998, p. 77). More often than not, tearful and sad I cried out for peace. Day by day the hopes and dreams I had built up have been shattered. Some days, remembering the stillness and light that I experienced with Fran in conscious dying eluded me. I just wanted to dig in my heels and shout, 'I don't want to do this alone!' And yet other days I was awake and alive with hope and purpose.

One of the most enduring and unexpected outcomes of grief is the deep personal need to be still in nature, to care for the soul and cultivate silence. In the deepest days of grief, walking kept my head together. Just. Every day, walking in nature continues to teach me to live in the moment, to slow down, take small steps, to breathe, there is no panic, no rush, all is well and all is connected. Inspired by Kumar (1992, 2015), as I walk, I come to want and need less and less of physical, material things and seek only peace and stillness amidst the confusion and mess:

'Greenness grew over the brown beds, which, freshening daily suggested the thought, that hope traversed them at night and left each morning brighter traces of her steps,' (Brontë, 1847/1995, p. 107).

Trodding a familiar path one day, something deep was triggered as I remembered the ancient spiritual practice of walking the labyrinth and a subtle and subconscious tie to remembering purpose emerged. The ancient path of the labyrinth, unlike a maze has one path, always leading in to the centre and out to the same starting point. On returning home, my son presents me with a pebble he found on the beach – a perfect spiral, carved by nature and tossed out as a gift to the discerning traveller. This is not unusual, as throughout our family life, symbols of hearts, spirals and labyrinths have marked our way, manifest in Fran's sculptures, in multiple, mutual gifts and love tokens and even on my wedding ring. The symbol of the labyrinth marks Fran's grave. I ponder these symbols and archetypes that have been staring me in the face for years! Perhaps they were clues to walking the ancient path of remembering, in youth and early nursing career with Liam in Denver and with Fran in conscious dying; all are turns in the labyrinth. It is the same path over and over again but this time it is one of grief and loss. A path, which invites me to stay awake and to remember purpose. A path, which holds the light for me when sadness descends. A path allowing others to walk alongside me, when the days are just too hard. Remembering purpose is sometimes stepping back and holding the intention of caring, healing love and light when others do not want you alongside them. This is just one turn of the labyrinth. Pausing at the centre, I close the chapter, turn and continue along the path, sometimes walking alongside, other times welcoming others to walk alongside me.

My heart cries as I remember again
that walking alongside is what you are here to do.
I saw with fresh eyes, the ancient path of labyrinth.
I had forgotten.
Walking transcended pain, fragile traces of her steps
All is connected.
So this is how a broken heart heals.
Grief rumbles on. Mud settles.
I pause. It's painful.
In the uncertain hour I walk.
Alone in the labyrinth, deer, holding the light, emerge,
Inviting me to walk alongside, in nature.
There is sad peace.
Walking alongside has offered a hand, strong and ancient.
I am honoured.
Crying out for remembering purpose when
dreams are shattered,
I walk in sacred space, the discerning traveller.
A single mum, no one ever told me that
when sadness descends,
swirling pain reflects loving relationships – the pain,
chasing, excruciating.
I am afraid but the labyrinth stirs soul, fluttering in hearts,
tossed amidst the chaos of howled, unsettled parenting,
in grief, in caring, my life fractured.
Everyday, I am her author.
The only truth I know, that young men need
someone who is healing their pain and frustrated hopes.
I present the poetry of walking the path.
It hurts. Take small steps. Be still.
Witnessing labyrinths in nature I remember
healing and patience tie my heart to life.
Be still my son, hear,
be still. Joy speaks again.

Chapter 10

The soul is more ancient than consciousness and mind. Each day your soul weaves
your life together. It weaves the opaque and ancient depth of you with the actual
freshness of your present experience. The soul is the home of memory.
(O'Donohue, 1997, p. 297)

As I found myself walking alongside Fran as he lived his dying,
gently awakening to a new reality, I had a bizarre yet profound
realisation that I had done it before and if I trusted my body and my
intuition, all would be well. As our lives turned into chaos, I began
to let go of expectations and logical plans and attempted to live in
the moment, as was his wish, and amidst it all, the profound sense of
remembering my purpose resonated. Everything I had ever done, felt
or experienced was in order to live the days we shared, from diagnosis
to his last breath and beyond, into the long and dark days of grief and
my still ongoing adjustment to life without him. It has been said that
women are instinctively in touch with birth and death and that the
ancestral memory of the ebb and flow of life's transitions is, 'in our
bones' (Warner, 2013, p. 32). Being alongside, as souls move in and
out of this mortal coil, bodies unwind and unravel on the threshold of
life and death; the feminine is there in the raw pain and mess, holding
space for dignity and love.

Sustaining dignity and love in life's most vulnerable moments
is what keeps us human and as old memories surfaced, the sense
of knowing and my connection to childbirth grew stronger but it
was far from a comfortable feeling. I remember it was horrible and
undignified and I hated how the professional, private and prudish
young woman that had entered the hospital became, within hours,
a bellowing wild animal. As my body took over, somehow knowing
what to do, the rest of me followed. With hormones raging, riding
the waves of pain was instinctive and soon forgotten but the shame
lingered, dragging me into murky, unknown waters. 'Oh you leave
your dignity at the door when you come in 'ere love,' the chirpy
midwife reassured me. It didn't help. Childbirth is steeped in

conspiracies of silence, taboos and forbidden subjects that are off limits because they are too distasteful and humiliating. Shoved to the edges of memory because they are too painful or embarrassing, my mother's voice reminds me that some things are never to be mentioned in polite company. And so it is with death.

When both our children came into this world I experienced what could only be described as a bolt of electricity coming out of my chest and connecting with the same energy coming from the babies. It was visible, tangible. By Fran's graveside I had the same sensation. Astonishingly, this detail is identified by Rinpoche in *The Tibetan book of living and dying*, where he describes 'a shaft of light springing from the heart is a moment of enlightened energy' (1992, p. 277). Similarly, in her autobiography, *Expecting Adam*, Martha Beck described her pregnancy as 'a feeling rising around me like a tide … like polar opposite magnets, reaching through a blank space, rearranging things into a new order' (1999, p. 39). She goes on to tell how she came to learn to pay attention to the feeling, explaining that the, 'sense of knowing feels a lot like remembering something that is not past but future. It has never been wrong' (p. 298). In the painful, dark and lonely days and nights that followed, staying awake to that connection in the unavoidable intensity of grief and complexity of bereavement was a different story. Sometimes I just wanted to howl like a wounded animal to release the pain inside me. Howling is underrated. It is acceptable, even encouraged in childbirth, but in death we avoid it because the rawness of the pain is too hard to contemplate. However, my journal reminds me that amidst the darkness there was stillness and remembering, my inner voice reminding me that all is well, do not be frightened. Go deep and allow what you know to come to the fore. Let your intuition guide you and remember you have done this before.

Like childbirth, dying can be a messy business. Certainly, the abandonment of dignity and the emergence of an extreme vulnerability evident in childbirth also arises in dying, as if in a unitary rhythm connecting across time. I remember how, when Fran first became unwell he was admitted to the hospital for emergency investigations. Calling me in tears and distress, I rushed to him. Finding him alone on a busy surgical ward, he was weak and disorientated from a biopsy procedure. Changing his bloodstained sheets was reminiscent of labour, when quietly and without fuss he cared for me. Nothing could fix him but I hope that just being alongside helped. The shift from professional to patient wasn't easy, especially at times when Fran was at his most restless and vulnerable. Now a widow and single mum I am regularly invited to share my story at teacher training days and conferences. Standing in front of audiences of experts I tell a sobering truth, of how, almost on the flip of a coin, fate decided that our roles would be transformed and now we have become the problem that they, the professionals, talk about. It was and is humiliating and humbling but death is the ultimate leveller.

In recounting a tale of the Buddha, Rinpoche (1992) stated that 'there is only one law of the universe that never changes – that all things change, and that all things are impermanent' (p. 29), a view supported by Sheldrake (2013) who argued that a delusion of science is that 'the laws of nature are fixed and will stay the same forever' (p. 7). Describing the emotions of witnessing a birth for the first time, Levine (1986) wrote of the experience as a paradox of fear and joy, pain and laughter, connecting him to his humanity at its most physical and instinctive level. He went on to assert that, 'acknowledging impermanence holds the key to life itself' (p. 3). Nothing is fixed in time and space, change is a constant reality and yet humanity struggles to hold on, control events and even life itself, disconnecting us from instinctual deep inner knowledge. It would appear that every time an individual switches on the television or logs on to the Internet, life transitions, death and life are loathed and celebrated in equal measure. Scores of deaths are witnessed every day, from natural disasters, war and hunger, fear of terrorism and of 'other,' is palpable. In what would seem like an obscene contrast, celebrities parade their flawless lives and perfect babies across the pages of glossy magazines. And yet, what connects these apparently opposite scenarios and invokes human interest is an unspoken, clandestine bond that is impermanence itself, a paradox of denial of change and yet an acknowledgement of its inevitability.

Until the middle of the 20th century, birth and death were very much a part of life in every community in the United Kingdom. This is not least illustrated in Victorian art and literature, for example the death of little Nell is described vividly in Charles Dickens's

Old curiosity shop (Dickens, 1840/1995), as is the death of Helen
in Charlotte Brontë's *Jane Eyre* (Brontë, 1847/1995). Indeed, until
the creation of the National Health Service in 1948, the majority
of people were born and died within their own homes, cared for
by their families, loved ones and the wise men and women of the
neighbourhood, like my grandmother (Warner, 2013). Although this
has remained a reality in many places in the world, in the West, these
life events have been relegated to hospitals and care settings. Within
three generations death has become almost a new phenomenon, as
the beginning and end of life in many instances has become void
of meaningful ritual, hidden and pushed to the margins of society
(O'Donohue, 1997, 2000; Warner, 2011, 2013). But we need to talk
about it. We must. At the precipice, we cannot rescue or fix. At the
precipice we can only love, serve and remember that letting go of the
illusion of certainty and immortality may deepen our desire to live in
the moment.

Naturally in touch with the cycle of life and death and with
intuitive knowledge of the body's rhythms, women have historically
supported others in birthing and in dying (Estés, 1992). It is
heartening to see that these skills are re-emerging, as there is a
movement to reclaim the sacred and honour the dying (O'Donohue,
2000; Warner, 2013). Possibly as a result of desperate need, a
collective remembering, or both an increasing number of individuals
are following their intuition, reawakening their skills and offering
end of life companionship as death doulas (Tucker, 2014), soul
companions (O'Donohue, 1997), soul apprentices (Kearney, 2007)
or soul midwives (Warner, 2011, 2013). In taking their rightful
place alongside loved ones as partners, friends, volunteers, therapists,
ministers, nurses and doctors all are awakening to the instinctive
human skill of helping transition to come, peacefully and without fear.

Chapter 11

*Helping to move towards a more humane and moral
community and civilization, we move from Caritas to
Communitas. (Watson, 2018, p. 46)*

But I had missed something. In caring for Fran, I gave my all and
honestly believe I held him and everyone around in compassion. I
could do no other. I was patient, listened and supportive when others
told me how awful it was for them, but as time went on it left me
drained and exhausted. Time and again, when I thought I had no
more to give, somehow I managed to keep going. In the early days
and months of my bereavement I was repeatedly told to, 'Look after
myself,' but I had absolutely no idea about what that meant, or what
to do. I was just trying to survive. Once again, in grief and desolation,
I turned to a safe place, books. I revisited Caring Science textbooks
and notes from my Denver days. I saw something that I had never
seen before, something that had been invisible for over 20 years and
it was like a light coming on, the proverbial penny dropping. The
notion of self/other is key to Caring Science and is written in that
way to remind us of the oneness of the connection (Watson, 2018).
Given my background and early influences it was not surprising that
in my mind, self was equated with selfishness and I had been blind to
fully understanding how self matters in a unitary caring relationship.
My gut instinct tells me that I am not alone here and that denial of
self is an innate condition for many mothers, wives and daughters.
Through a lens of Caring Science, we are reminded that if we are in
true, authentic relationship with others, then we are important too. If
compassion is to flourish, then practising loving kindness to oneself
is essential. Listening, being sensitive to one's own needs, treating
oneself with dignity and remembering that I matter is at the heart of
caring practice.

In order to pin down the essence of caring, Watson defined
what are known as the caritas processes® (Watson, 2018). Latin
in origin, caritas means love of or charity for humankind and

processes denotes that this is ongoing and unfolding. Thus, the caritas
processes represent a flow of caring energy and are an invitation
and challenge to be mindful of this love, not only in relationships
with others, but towards our planet and ourselves. If nursing is to
survive as a discipline, it must be grounded in philosophy and ethics
and have a moral base (Watson, 2018). Furthermore, it must own a
language of caring proudly, thus making it visible and taking away
the awkwardness and shame of admitting love. Remembering that
in Caring Science YOU MATTER, the caritas processes invite key
questions, encouraging the user to frame thoughts and actions in a
language and context of caring, applying it to self and other. On a
personal level this has taken a long time to grasp and learning to see
in a new way is a continual challenge. Grounded in
the caritas processes I ask:

- Am I being kind and compassionate to myself
  as well as others?
  (This is known as practising loving kindness.)

- Am I being authentic and enabling others to be
  themselves too?

- Am I being sensitive to myself and others?
  Am I fully present to make this a moment of caring?

- How can I develop and sustain loving, trusting,
  caring relationships?

- How can I listen honestly to another's story,
  remaining open to hear the positive and the negative?

- Rather than focusing on problems, how can I use a
  language of caring to be creative in seeking solutions?

- Is my teaching/learning helpful and meaningful to
  myself and others?

- Am I paying attention in creating a healing, safe and caring environment – what makes a difference here?

- Seeing all interactions with others as an honour and a privilege, how do I uphold human dignity (for myself too!)?

- Am I being open to what I don't know and accepting of what I don't understand?

Applying the caritas processes to self inevitably means that it seeps into life and our closest relationships. It reminds us that it is okay just to be, and to no longer constantly take responsibility for fixing and doing, to breath and pause, allowing ourselves to be mindful, in the moment. It becomes how we are in the world, and helps us to remember and to hold on to who we are. Having to think about the ten caritas processes may be off-putting at first, even overwhelming, but in essence they are not separate entities at all, rather they are a flow of increasing awareness, an unfolding spectrum of human potential. However, it may be that there are one or two that are personally more helpful than others at any given moment. The three caritas processes that help me most are the ones that prompt the questions: am I practising loving kindness, am I listening and am I upholding human dignity for myself and others?

In grief, as I recognised and remembered that before is part of the now and what we lived then will be part of the future, the essence of Caring Science emerged, re-patterning life experiences. Liam and I walked only a short path together but the time we shared was profound. In a short life that had been so deprived of affection, love and touch, the nurses acted with intention and intuitive knowing, showing him a special kind of love. I have carried that time in my heart and through the caring moments I witnessed in the wee small hours of a few January nights in 1984, emerged not only nursing role models but the values and ethics that I have come to live by. Rilke reminds us that, 'In the middle of transition … the future enters into us … to transform itself in us long before it happens' (Rilke, 1934/1993, p. 64). Everything led to being with Fran in the last 92 days we had together and flowed beyond, to doctoral studies, this book, and days that are forever new to me now as I adjust to life without him. Through a lens of Caring Science, my story was transformed to become a research study (Biley, 2018), an offering I make with gratitude and intention, to honour and to give something back to nursing.

From a unitary Caring Science perspective, understanding what it means to be human requires research that is experienced and not necessarily analysed, acknowledging that creativity, poetic accounts and metaphor may accurately communicate life experience (Watson, 2012). With this in mind, I set out to deconstruct and reconstruct my story, to see past encounters and present realities in new ways but dwelling with the caritas processes of being authentically present, being open to new ways of learning, of being, becoming, belonging and being open to mystery. Referencing Fran's academic work and art, layering in literature, poetry, journals, music, emails and Sarah Hough's beautiful drawings, a transformative rhythm of living dying, love and grief emerged. Even gifts we had exchanged over the years – spirals, hearts and labyrinths – became part of the tapestry of the autoethnography as gifts and love tokens led to the right data.

In January 2016, a book landed on the doormat. In it was a chapter written by Fran. It was his last academic work on what is known as the cut-up technique (Biley, 2016), and served as a reminder that even 4 years after his death, Fran was indeed 'still here-there-everywhere in this pandimensional universe,' (Todaro-Franceschi, 2006, p. 298). Cut-ups were first introduced as poetry by the Dadaist poet Tristan Tzara in the 1920s who, in describing the poetic approach stated:

Take a newspaper
Take some scissors
Choose from this paper an article of the length you
want to make your poem.
Cut out the article.
Next carefully cut out each of the words that makes up
this article and put them all in a bag.
Shake gently.
Next take out each cutting one after the other.
Copy conscientiously in the order in which they
left the bag.
The poem will resemble you. (Colman, n. d.)

However, it wasn't until the 1960s that the cut-up technique
was used most notably by the Beat author William Burroughs.
In this process the author literally would take a text and cut it up,
then put it back together randomly to create a new text. The idea of
deconstructing and reconstructing language was to break through the
barriers and frustration of words and more accurately describe the
chaotic and non-linear, or unitary universe, to create new meaning,
new realities and consciousness (Biley, 2016; Biley, 2018). First
delving into the Beat Generation literature in the early 1990s whilst
we travelled in India, Fran developed a life-long affinity with the
genre, particularly the work of Jack Kerouac, Alan Ginsberg and
William Burroughs. Fran then found a way to combine his passion
for poetry and literature with nursing and academic practice. By
applying a cut-up technique to stories of human experience in a
nursing/health field of consciousness, students were invited to see in
a new way.

I remember being profoundly moved by Fran's first attempt to test
out the cut-up technique. It was a presentation in which he told the
story of a close friend and the death of his young son, who drowned
whilst on holiday in Europe. Experiencing the cut-up version of the
tragedy left the audience reeling and in tears. Fran was always an
individual who pushed boundaries and I was uncomfortable, feeling
that it reached a depth of intimacy and human pain that was almost
too excruciatingly personal to share. However, I remember discussing
it with our friend, who said that it gave an accurate representation

of the chaos and randomness of the events and the turmoil and indiscriminate feelings and emotions at the time, thus supporting Burroughs's claim that, 'life is a cut up, full of random interjections' (Biley, 2004, p. 142). Over the years, Fran honed the craft of the cut-up as a unitary approach to teaching and scholarly work, and true to his pandimensional style, this continued with a posthumous publication (Biley, 2016).

When the book arrived through the door, I remembered our dear friend and his son, both now dead and decided that I too would take a chance and use the cut-up technique to explore grief, remembering and moments of caring and caritas. A chapter in *A handbook for Caring Science* (2018) details how the cut-up technique became my research method. Creating my own caring ritual, in quiet space, I lit a candle. Cutting up sections of the text, one section at a time, I placed the cut-up words and phrases in a wooden bowl, then randomly stuck the words on to paper, transposed it into a Word document, and dwelt with the new text. At the end of Chapter 12 you will find the cut-up version of this story, which illustrates how meaning emerged as poetic prose, creating a caritas language of grief and remembering (Biley, 2018). The cut-up technique was used at different stages in the research and in writing this book, to invite a pause, for reflection and stillness, Fran's words resonating … 'When seeing, how do you see? When thinking how do you think?' Throughout the process, the cut-ups revealed new depth of meaning, always challenging what I thought I knew. For example, in spite of my attempt to live in the moment, to seek stillness and to let the mud settle, the cut-ups confronted me, revealing hidden exhaustion, fear and confusion. I was not enough /Fran took my all / I tried. As in life, so in death, Fran was always a man of profound dignity and holding him as he transitioned, the cut-up revealed that silent dignity was remembering purpose.

In the uncertain hour that was death and grief, I hit an ethical wall. How could I write about life as a single, widowed mum when our lives were falling apart? Telling a story such as this carries moral responsibility, to do no harm and protect the vulnerability of self and other. And yet bearing witness to what happened is in itself an ethical and moral act (Frank, 2013). As an ethical principle our children and close family members have not been included in this story. They have their own story to tell, their own music to make and their own poetry to share. On the verge of pulling out of the doctorate process I spoke to my supervisor who advised me not to write about what was happening, but to write about how it made me feel. Unitary Caring Science's fundamental ethic of facing humanity and the values of the caritas processes reached out, took my hand and guided me through. And so I wrote about walking in nature, how I walked and howled and walked some more, until I could face going home again. The cut-ups told me that tossed amidst the chaos of howled unsettled parenting, swirling pain reflects loving relationships and that everyday I was her author and it was at this point that the cut-up revealed the metaphor of labyrinth as remembering purpose and the secret that the birds hold, that we continue to walk the same path of tears, hope and joy.

Chapter 12

We were never really born, we will never really die ... There's nothing to be afraid of and nothing to be glad about. I know this from staring at mountains months on end. They never show any expression, they are like empty space. Do you think the emptiness of space will ever crumble away? Mountains will crumble, but the emptiness of space, which is the one universal essence of mind, the vast awakener hood, empty and awake, will never crumble away because it was never born. (Kerouac, 1957/1999, p. 7)

Against impossible odds, my doctorate was completed, as weeks somehow have turned into months, and incredibly, months into years. In living his dying, his last master class, Fran taught that living in the now is all there is but life remains an unpredictable and uncertain path. Just when I think I am getting it together, my head reverts into a puddle of mush. I am reminded of the early weeks following childbirth, when the world seemed to go along without me. Even on good days, the gurgle of grief snares unexpectedly and traps me inside a bubble of exhaustion and tears. I just want to dig in my heels and shout, I don't want to do this! But as ever, life demands that I must. In an auto-ethnographic account of grief, following the death of her daughter, Terry (2012) describes a loss of purpose in stating, 'My sense of purpose, the thing that has guided my life has dissipated. My belief in happily ever after, and fate and purpose … gone' (p. 363). And yet, over the 3 year study period, the author goes on to illustrate how grief and pain were transformed as new meaning and purpose emerged, stating that, 'I want to plot my path intentionally… I will never sweat the small stuff again. I will take the time to enjoy the beauty of the world,' (p. 363). For so long, the future was blank, but amidst and in spite of the fog and turbulence of everyday life, green shoots of life and hope are emerging.

Like crumbs of the old, slabbed snow,
That all but barricaded London
The day your bird broke free and the glass dome
Vanished – with a ringing sound
I thought it was a telephone.
I knew the glass had gone and the bird had gone.
Like lifting an eyelid I peered for the glass -
But I knew it had gone. Because of the huge
Loose emptiness of light
Wheeling through everything.
As if a gecko
Fell into empty light.
(Hughes, 1998, p. 78)

Fran lived mindfulness in conscious dying and I was privileged to be with him in a human-to-human loving connection. Death does not end a relationship it simply shifts 'from loving in presence to loving in absence,' (Malinski, 2012, p. 242). Taking small steps and finding stillness in nature, I have learned to be kind to myself. I sleep alone now under my pastel duvet with not so new pillows. My space is solid and cosy, my only company, a little dog who cuddles and clings as close as she can, the guardian of my dreams as Virginia Woolf would say. Her breath, her doggie smell and physical bodily warmth of 'other' offer some comfort and security. It is enough. I am grateful. I am not ready for anything more.

Remembering was a constant thread, connecting across time. Being with Fran in conscious dying connected me to childbirth, stirring the sense that I knew what to do and if I trusted this instinct all would be well. As memories twinge, time is meaningless. When pregnant with my second child, we moved house. I recall that our new neighbour was an older man and a bit of a dodgy character but he was friendly enough and was excited at the prospect of a new baby next door. Man to man, Fran shared the anxiety of an expectant father – how could he ever be enough? Our neighbour laughed and said, 'Don't worry about that son, the baby brings the love, you will be fine.' We never forgot that truth and remained forever grateful for his wisdom. Part of me died with Fran but love stays. I will never be the same but the agony of grief no longer smothers me. I can remember, let go and move forward without abandoning the love. In the ebb and flow of life and death, love is the constant. At the edge of transition, a new reality invites stillness and peace and reminds us that in these moments, upholding dignity is what keeps us human. In trusting the inner voice of feminine wisdom I understand that Fran was right: as the mud settles, all is well. I know what to do, I've done it before.

Cut-up of the story

Before was part of the now and what we lived then will
be part of the future.
To walk alongside in nature is how a broken heart heals.
Gentleness of poets trace steps
and joy is found in the patience of living caritas.
Remembering purpose? The sensation is like resilience,
strength
and patience, shaking memory.
I was privileged to be with him.
In sacred space, healing and patience tie my heart to life.
Walking spirals of caring reveals the story,
stay awake, round and round.
Tossed amidst the chaos of howled unsettled parenting,
unfolding moments held witness.
A white cheek. By the pond,
in the mirrored image, my heart cries as I remember again,
that walking alongside is what you are here to do.
Don't be frightened.
Caring theory, spreading out its roots,
in remembering childbirth, bearing fear, body and soul,
I knew what to do.
Every day I am her author.
Witnessing labyrinths in nature,
I remember a story of a soul journey, healing and service.
Unitary consciousness, like fine wrinkles, pattern became
truth.
Remembering purpose, the discerning traveller
will be sensitive to cultivating patience.
Embraced in nursing practice, I lived human Caring Science,
walking alongside the vulnerable must be lived if it is to mean
anything at all.
My life fractured, I found myself by his bedside.
As he transitioned I was alone.

I remembered in walking alongside, there is sad peace.
These ways of being – a deep knowing and intuition,
ethically disciplined behaviour, loving kindness,
became remembering purpose.
I present the jewelled poetry of walking the path.
Re -arranging, re-patterning time and mind,
mystery weaves, memory twinges,
my inner voice tells me that all will be well. I had done it before.
The dying are our teachers, visible and tangible lived experience.
Remembering purpose was devastating.
Wounded women who are extraordinary offer the gift of
dreams to live again,
when dreams are shattered, when the soul reared with chaos,
cherished poems awaken care, love, intention.
Mother becoming consciousness across deep raging storms,
be still.
Allow what you know to come to the fore.
Walking alongside, I washed his suffering.
I take small steps, path of labyrinth, fresh roses.
Mud settles
in the strangest places, how do we see a sacred path?
The birds feel that it is the same path of tears, hope and joy.
Re-patterning birth, his paintings spoke poetry,
of fluttering hearts, deep inner knowing, intimacy and comfort,
sacred feminine, strength and mystery.
Be still my son ...
In everyday life, purpose determined that I reach out,
the paradox of the unknown. All is connected.
I stand alone in the labyrinth,
nursing memories, mindful touch, transcended pain,
simple humanity, compassion in the uncertain hour.
In the silent sense of dignity ponder caring presence,
the key to caring values echoes the deepest places of the heart.
Nursing transformed into living purpose.

Ancient remembering, in vigil,
one path capturing gems secretly,
healing anger. Grief rumbles on. It hurts.
In the uncertain hour I walk, the soul, nesting.
I remember my love, caring intention,
waves of blessing,
threads of soul.
I pause.
It is passed.

REFERENCES

Aynsley-Green, A. (2018). *The British betrayal of childhood*.
    London: Routledge.

Beck, M. (1999). *Expecting Adam*. London: Piatkus.

Belenky, M. F., Clinchy, B. M., Goldberger, N. R., & Tarule, J. M.
    (1997). *Women's ways of knowing (10th anniversary
    edition)*. New York: Perseus Books.

Bennett, A. (2004). *The history boys*. London: Faber & Faber.

Biley, A. (1997). 'A caring moment: The rose'. *European Nurse*,
    1(3), 55.

Biley, A. (2000). 'Mother: A sacred moment'. *Sacred Space*, 2, 1.

Biley, A. (2018). 'Remembering purpose: An autoethnography'. In
    W. Rosa, S.Horton-Deutsch & J. Watson (Eds.), *A handbook
    for Caring Science* (pp. 633 – 641). New York: Springer.

Biley, A., & Giovannoni, J. (2018). 'Pondering forgiveness in a
    unitary Caring Science paradigm: A reflection'.
    International Journal of Human Caring 22:3, 140 – 46.

Biley, F. C. (1992). 'Out of the frame'. *Nursing Times, 5*(2), 19 – 20.

Biley, F. C. (1998). 'An experiment in accessing pandimensionality:
    The literary poetics and deconstruction techniques of
    William S. Burroughs applied to the science of Unitary
    Human Beings'. Unpublished paper presented to the 7th
    Rogerian Conference, Nursing and the changing person-
    environment. June 19 – 21, New York: New York University.

Biley, F. C. (2004). 'Postmodern literary poetics of experience: A new form of aesthetic enquiry'. In F. Rapport (ed.), *New qualitative methodologies in health and social care research* (pp. 139 – 149). London: Routledge.

Biley, F. C. (2010). 'In search of mindfulness'. *International Journal of Healing and Caring,* 10, 1.

Biley, F. C. (2016). 'Waking up following breast surgery: An insight from the Beats, Burroughs and the cut up technique'. In K. T. Galvin and M. Prendergast (eds.), *Poetic inquiry II* (pp. 205 – 210). Rotterdam: Sense.

Black Elk, W., & Lyon, W. S. (1990). *Black Elk: The sacred ways of a Lakota.* New York: Harper Collins.

Bowman, T. (1994). *Loss of dreams: A special kind of grief.* Personal publication.

Brittain, V. (1933/1978). *Testament of youth.* London: Virago.

Brontë, C. (1847). *Jane Eyre.* London: Penguin (1995 edn).

Byock, I. (2014). *The four things that matter most – 10th anniversary edition.* London: Atria.

Carlick, A., & Biley, F. C. (2004). 'Thoughts on the therapeutic use of narrative in the promotion of coping with cancer'. *European Journal of Cancer Care,* 13, 308 – 11.

Colman, D. (n. d.). *William S. Burroughs on the art of cut-up writing.* Retrieved from: www.openculture.com

Conway, K. (1997). *Ordinary life: A memoir of illness.* New York: Freeman.

Cowling, W. R. (2012). 'Healing as appreciating wholeness'. In W. K. Cody (ed.), *Philosophical and theoretical perspectives for advanced nursing practice* (5th ed, pp. 119 – 137). Burlington, VT: Jones & Bartlett.

Dass, R. (n.d.). Retrieved from: http://www.ramdass.org/learning-to-grieve

Debold, E., Tolman, D., & Mikel Brown, L. (1996). 'Embodying knowledge, knowing desire: Authority and split subjectivities in girls' epistemological development'. In N. Goldberger, J. Tarule, B. Clinchy, & N. Belenky (eds.), *Knowledge, difference and power* (pp. 85 – 125). New York: Basic Books.

Denzin, N. K. (2014). *Interpretive autoethnography*. London: Sage.

Dickens, C. (1840). *The old curiosity shop* London: Wordsworth. (1995 ed).

Eliot, T. S. (1944). *Four quartets*. London: Faber & Faber (published, 1959).

Ellis, C., & Bochner, A. (2000). 'Autoethnography, personal narrative, reflexivity: Researcher as subject'. In N.K. Denzin, & Y. S. Lincoln (eds.), *Handbook of qualitative research* (2nd ed, pp. 733 – 68). Thousand Oaks, CA: Sage.

Estés, C. P. (1992). *Women who run with the wolves*. London: Rider.

Everything But the Girl (1994). *We walk the same line*. Amplified Heart (CD Recording). Warner Music Ltd.

Frank, A. W. (2013). *The wounded storyteller* (2nd ed). Chicago: University of Chicago Press.

Frankel, V. E. (1946/1984). *Man's search for meaning*. New York: Washington Square Press.

Frankel, V. E. (1946/2012). *The doctor and the soul*. London: Souvenir Press.

Gibran, K. (1926/1991). *The prophet*. London: Pan Books.

Gibran, K. (1995). *The voice of Kahlil Gibran*. R. Waterfield (Ed.). London: Penguin.

Goldberger, N. (1996a). 'Looking backward, looking forward'. In N. Goldberger, J.Tarule, B. Clinchy, & N. Belenky (eds), *Knowledge, difference and power* (pp. 1 – 21). New York: Basic Books.

Goldberger, N. (1996b). 'Cultural imperatives and diversity in ways of knowing'. In N. Goldberger, J. Tarule, B. Clinchy, & N. Belenky (eds.), *Knowledge, difference and power* (pp. 335 – 71). New York: Basic Books.

Halifax, J. (2008). *Being with dying*. Boston: Shambhala.

Halifax, J. (2018). *Standing at the edge*. New York: Flatiron Books.

Hesse, H. (1956/1995). *The journey to the East*. London: Picador

.

Hesse, H. (2011). *The seasons of the soul*. Berkeley: North Atlantic Books.

H. H. Dalai Lama (1997). *Healing anger*. New York: Snow Lion Publications.

H. H. Dalai Lama (1999). *Ancient wisdom, modern world*. London: Little, Brown & Company.

Horton-Deutsch, S. , & Anderson, J. (2018). *Caritas coaching*. Indianapolis, IN: Sigma Theta Tau.

Hughes, T. (1998). *Birthday letters*. London: Faber & Faber.

Jonas-Simpson, C. (2010). 'Awakening to space consciousness and timeless transcendent presence'. *Nursing Science Quarterly*, 23(3), 195 – 200.

Kearney, M. (2007). *Mortally wounded: stories of soul pain, death and healing*. New Orleans, LA: Spring Journal Books.

Kendall-Raynor, P. (2018). 'More than 17,000 younger nurses leave the NHS'. Retrieved from: *rcni.com/nursing-standard/ newsroom/news 17th January, 2018*.

Kerouac, J. (1957/1999). *Jack Kerouac selected letters 1957 – 1969*. A. Charters (ed.), New York: Penguin.

Kübler-Ross, E., & Kessler, D. (2000). *Life lessons*. London: Simon & Schuster.

Kumar, S. (1992). *No destination*. Totnes, Devon: Resurgence Books.

Kumar, S. (2015). *Soil, soul, society*. Lewes, East Sussex: Leaping Hare Press.

Lao Tzu (n.d.). *Tao Te Ching*. London: Penguin. (1963 ed).

Levine, S. (1986). *Who dies?* Bath: Gateway.

Lewis, C. S. (1961). *A grief observed*. London: Faber and Faber.

Liu, X., Wei, X., Wang, Y., Williams, M. G., Geng, Y., Zhang, Q., & Liu, X. (2013). 'Can inner peace be improved by mindfulness training: A randomized control trial'. Retrieved from: *Stress and Health:* www.wileyonlinelibrary.com (DOI: 10.1002/smi.2551).

Malinski, V. M. (2012). 'Meditations on the unitary rhythm of dying-grieving'. *Nursing Science Quarterly, 25*(3), 239 – 44.

Manthey, M. (1980). *The practice of primary nursing*. London: Blackwell.

Newman, M. A. (2008). *Transforming presence*. Philadelphia, PA: FA Davis.

Nightingale, F. (1859/2010). *Notes on nursing*. Milton Keynes: Digireads.com

O'Donohue, J. (1997). *Anam cara*. London: Bantam.

O'Donohue, J. (2000). *Eternal echoes*. London: Bantam.

Perrett, S. E., & Biley, F. C. (2013a). 'A Roy model study of adapting to being HIV positive'. *Nursing Science Quarterly, 26*(4), 337 – 43.

Perrett, S. E., & Biley, F. C. (2013b). 'Negotiating uncertainty: The transitional process of adapting to life with HIV'. *Journal of the Association of Nurses in AIDS Care,* 24(3), 207 – 18.

Reeder, F. (2013). 'What will count as evidence in the year 2050?' In W. K. Cody (ed.), *Philosophical and theoretical perspectives for advanced nursing practice* (5th ed, pp. 353 – 58). Burlington, VT: Jones & Bartlett.

Renz, M. (2015). *Dying a transition*. New York: Columbia University Press.

Rilke, R. M. (1934/1993). *Letters to a young poet*. New York: W. W. Norton & Company.

Rinpoche, S. (1992). *The Tibetan book of living and dying*. London: Rider.

Rogers, M. E. (1970). *An introduction to the theoretical basis of nursing*. Philadelphia, PA: FA Davis.

Rosa, W., Horton-Deutsch, S., & Watson, J. (2018). *A handbook for caring science*. New York: Springer.

Sheldrake, R. (2013). *The science delusion*. London: Hodder & Stoughton.

Simon, P. (1965/2004). *Kathy's song*. Simon & Garfunkel: Old friends. (CD Recording). Sony Music.

Suzuki, D. T. (1999). 'Introduction'. In E. Herrigel (ed.), *Zen in the art of archery*, (pp. vii – x). New York: Vintage Spiritual Classics.

Tacón, A. M. (2011). 'Mindfulness: Existential, loss and grief factors in women with breast cancer'. *Journal of Psychosocial Oncology, 29*, 643 – 56.

Terry, A. W. (2012). 'My journey in grief: A mother's experience following the death of her daughter'. *Qualitative Inquiry, 18*(4), 355 – 67.

Thorn, T. (2015). 'Protection'. *Solo songs and collaborations, 1982 – 2015*. (CD Recording). Caroline International.

Todaro-Franceschi, V. (2006). 'Studying synchronicity related to dead lived ones AKA after death communication: Martha, what do you think?' *Nursing Science Quarterly, 19*(4), 297 – 99.

Tolle, E. (2009). *Awakening in the now* (DVD Production). Boulder, CO: Sounds True.

Tucker, E. (2014). *Death doulas: Helping people to face up to dying*. Retrieved from: http://www.theguardian.com/lifestyle/deathanddying

Vanier, J. (1979). *Community and growth*. London: Darton, Longman & Todd.

Vanier, J. (1997). *Our journey home*. London: Hodder & Stoughton.

Warner, F. (2011). *A safe journey home*. London: Hay House.

Warner, F. (2013). *The soul midwives' handbook*. London: Hay House.

Watson, J. (1988). *Nursing: Human science and human care*. New York: National League for Nursing.

Watson, J. (1995). 'Postmodernism and knowledge development in nursing'. *Nursing Science Quarterly 8* (2), 60 – 4.

Watson, J. (1999). *Postmodern nursing and beyond*. London: Churchill Livingstone.

Watson, J. (2005). *Caring Science as sacred science*. Philadelphia, PA: FA Davis.

Watson, J. (2008). *Nursing: The philosophy and science of caring*. Rev. ed. Boulder, CO: University Press of Colorado.

Watson, J. (2012). *Human Caring Science*. Sudbury, MA: Jones & Bartlett.

Watson, J. (2018). *Unitary Caring Science*. Louisville, CO: University Press Colorado.

Wein, S. (2014). 'Spirituality: The psyche or the soul?' *Palliative and Supportive Care*, 12, 91 – 4.

West, M. (1981). *The clowns of God*. London: Hodder & Stoughton.

Wilber, K. (1993). *Grace and grit*. London: Shambhala.

Woodham-Smith, C. (1955). *Florence Nightingale*. London: Penguin.

Woolf, V. (1922/1981). *The diaries of Virginia Woolf, volume 2 1920 – 24*. London: Penguin.

Wright, S. G. (1994). *My patient – my nurse* (2nd ed). London: Scutari.

OTHER RESOURCES

'What is the cut up method?' (n.d.). Retrieved from: www.bbc.co.uk/news/magazine-33254672

From the wild moors of Brontë country where she was born, to the undulating soft landscape of Hardy's Dorset where she currently resides, all of her life Anna has been a collector of word gems for later use. Sparked by the 'duty of service' aspect of nursing she read about in the diaries of a First World War voluntary service nurse, Anna was inspired and has spent many years working in clinical nursing and in the voluntary sector in the UK Advanced work in Caring Science in the USA was to follow, and Anna recently completed her doctorate from the Watson Caring Science Institute. These days, Anna seeks stillness in walking every day with her little dog Dot. The 'love, serve, remember' she read about all those years ago is never far from her thoughts.

Watson Caring Science Institute

About Watson Caring Science Institute

Watson Caring Science Institute is an international non-profit 501C(3) organization that advances the unitary philosophies, theories and practices of 'Caring Science', developed by Dr. Jean Watson. Caring Science is a transdisciplinary approach that incorporates the art and science of nursing and includes concepts from the fields of philosophy, ethics, ecology and mind-body-spirit medicine.

There are an estimated 400 hospitals throughout the USA, in which their professional practice model is based upon Watson's philosophy and theory of human caring science. The institute has trained over 500 Caritas Coaches® globally to translate caring science theory into concrete human-to-human practices that help to repattern the culture of healthcare, whereby the practitioners 'live out' the theory in their professional and personal lives.

Focusing on research, education, practice, and leadership, Watson Caring Science Institute aims to deepen the development and understanding of Caring Science and Caritas Practices, to dramatically transform patient/family experiences of caring and healing in schools, hospitals, the wider community and our planet.

LOTUS
LIBRARY

About Lotus Library

Lotus Library is a publication imprint of Watson Caring Science Institute. Following from the philosophy of Caring Science, Lotus Library aims to encompass and showcase a humanitarian, human science orientation to human caring processes, phenomena and experiences. Our mission is rooted in compassionate care and healing of the mind-body-spirit as one. Our publications exemplify a transdisciplinary approach to sustaining caring/healing as a global covenant with humanity/Mother Earth. Lotus Library provides a forum for nurses and others to give voice to phenomena which otherwise may be ignored or dismissed, celebrating the mysteries of life, death suffering and joy, embracing the miracles of existence.

About Jean Watson

Dr. Jean Watson is Distinguished Professor and Dean Emerita, University of Colorado Denver, College of Nursing Anschutz Medical Center campus, where she held the nation's first endowed Chair in Caring Science for 16 years. She is founder of the original Center for Human Caring in Colorado and is a Fellow of the American Academy of Nursing; past President of the National League for Nursing; founding member of International Association in Human Caring and International Caritas Consortium. She is Founder and Director of the non-profit foundation, Watson Caring Science Institute (www.watsoncaringscience.org). In 2013 Dr. Watson was inducted as a Living Legend by the American Academy of Nursing, its highest honor. Her global work has resulted in her being awarded 15 Honorary Doctoral Degrees, 12, international.

As author/co-author of over 30 books on caring, her latest books range from empirical measurements and international research on caring, to new postmodern philosophies of caring and healing, philosophy and science of caring and unitary caring science as sacred science, global advance in caring literacy. Her books have received the American Journal of Nursing's "Book of the Year" award and seek to bridge paradigms as well as point toward transformative models, now, and the future.

.

For further Lotus Library reading visit our online store:
www.watsoncaringscience.org/the-caring-store/

CPSIA information can be obtained
at www.ICGtesting.com
Printed in the USA
FSHW011438240919

9 781733 123204